Library Edition

———

THE WIT AND HUMOR
OF AMERICA

In Ten Volumes

VOL. X

FRANK L. STANTON

THE
WIT AND HUMOR
OF AMERICA

EDITED BY
MARSHALL P. WILDER

Volume X

Funk & Wagnalls Company
New York and London

CONTENTS

CONTENTS

COMPLETE INDEX AT THE END OF VOLUME X.

TROUBLE-PROOF*

BY EDWIN L. SABIN

Never rains where Jim is—
    People kickin', whinin';
He goes round insistin',—
    "Sun is *almost* shinin'!"

Never's hot where Jim is—
    When the town is sweatin';
He jes' sets and answers,—
    "Well, *I* ain't a-frettin'!"

Never's cold where Jim is—
    None of *us* misdoubt it,
Seein' we're nigh frozen!
    He "ain't *thought* about it"!

Things that rile up others
    Never seem to strike him!
"Trouble-proof," I call it,—
    Wisht that I was like him!

*Lippincott's Magazine.

JOHNNY'S PA

BY WILBUR D. NESBIT

My pa—he always went to school,
  He says, an' studied hard.
W'y, when he's just as big as me
  He knew things by the yard!
Arithmetic? He knew it all
  From dividend to sum;
But when he tells me how it was,
  My grandma, she says "Hum!"

My pa—he always got the prize
  For never bein' late;
An' when they studied joggerfy
  He knew 'bout every state.
He says he knew the rivers, an'
  Knew all their outs an' ins;
But when he tells me all o' that,
  My grandma, she just grins.

My pa, he never missed a day
  A-goin' to the school,
An' never played no hookey, nor
  Forgot the teacher's rule;
An' every class he's ever in,
  The rest he always led.
My grandma, when pa talks that way,
  Just laughs an' shakes her head.

My grandma says 'at boys is boys,
    The same as pas is pas,
An' when I ast her what she means
    She says it is "because."
She says 'at little boys is best
    When they grows up to men,
Because they know how good they was,
    An' tell their children, then!

MAXIMS

BY BENJAMIN FRANKLIN

Never spare the parson's wine, nor the baker's pudding.

A house without woman or firelight is like a body without soul or spirit.

Kings and bears often worry their keepers.

Light purse, heavy heart.

He's a fool that makes his doctor his heir.

Ne'er take a wife till thou hast a house (and a fire) to put her in.

To lengthen thy life, lessen thy meals.

He that drinks fast pays slow.

He is ill-clothed who is bare of virtue.

Beware of meat twice boil'd, and an old foe reconcil'd.

The heart of a fool is in his mouth, but the mouth of a wise man is in his heart.

He that is rich need not live sparingly, and he that can live sparingly need not be rich.

He that waits upon fortune is never sure of a dinner.

NEVADA SKETCHES

BY SAMUEL L. CLEMENS

IN CARSON CITY

I feel very much as if I had just awakened out of
a long sleep. I attribute it to the fact that I have slept
the greater part of the time for the last two days and
nights. On Wednesday, I sat up all night, in Virginia,
in order to be up early enough to take the five o'clock
stage on Thursday morning. I was on time. It was
a great success. I had a cheerful trip down to Carson,
in company with that incessant talker, Joseph T. Good-
man. I never saw him flooded with such a flow of spirits
before. He restrained his conversation, though, until we
had traveled three or four miles, and were just crossing
the divide between Silver City and Spring Valley, when
he thrust his head out of the dark stage, and allowed a
pallid light from the coach lamps to illuminate his features for a moment, after which he returned to darkness
again, and sighed and said, "Damn it!" with some asper-
ity. I asked him who he meant it for, and he said, "The
weather out there." As we approached Carson, at about
half past seven o'clock, he thrust his head out again, and
gazed earnestly in the direction of that city—after which
he took it in again, with his nose very much frosted. He
propped the end of that organ upon the end of his finger,
and looked pensively upon it—which had the effect of

making him cross-eyed—and remarked, "O, damn it!"
with great bitterness. I asked him what was up this time,
and he said, "The cold, damp fog—it is worse than the
weather." This was his last. He never spoke again in
my hearing. He went on over the mountains with a lady
fellow passenger from here. That will stop his chatter,
you know, for he seldom speaks in the presence of ladies.

In the evening I felt a mighty inclination to go to a
party somewhere. There was to be one at Governor J.
Neely Johnson's, and I went there and asked permission
to stand around a while. This was granted in the most
hospitable manner, and the vision of plain quadrilles
soothed my weary soul. I felt particularly comfortable,
for if there is one thing more grateful to my feelings than
another, it is a new house—a large house, with its ceilings
embellished with snowy mouldings; its floors glowing
with warm-tinted carpets, with cushioned chairs and
sofas to sit on, and a piano to listen to; with fires so ar-
ranged you can see them, and know there is no humbug
about it; with walls garnished with pictures, and above
all mirrors, wherein you may gaze and always find something to admire, you know. I have a great regard for a
good house, and a girlish passion for mirrors. Horace
Smith, Esq., is also very fond of mirrors. He came and
looked in the glass for an hour with me. Finally it
cracked—the night was pretty cold—and Horace Smith's
reflection was split right down the centre. But where his
face had been the damage was greatest—a hundred cracks
converged to his reflected nose, like spokes from the hub
of a wagon wheel. It was the strangest freak the weather
has done this winter. And yet the parlor seemed warm
and comfortable, too.

About nine o'clock the Unreliable came and asked
Gov. Johnson to let him stand on the porch. The crea-

ture has got more impudence than any person I ever saw in my life. Well, he stood and flattened his nose against the parlor window, and looked hungry and vicious—he always looks that way—until Colonel Musser arrived with some ladies, when he actually fell in their wake and came swaggering in looking as if he thought he had been anxiously expected. He had on my fine kid boots, my plug hat, my white kid gloves (with slices of his prodigious hands grinning through the bursted seams), and my heavy gold repeater, which I had been offered thousands and thousands of dollars for many and many a time. He took those articles out of my trunk, at Washoe City, about a month ago, when we went there to report the proceedings of the convention. The Unreliable intruded himself upon me in his cordial way, and said, "How are you, Mark, old boy? When d'you come down? It's brilliant, ain't it? Appear to enjoy themselves, don't they? Lend a fellow two bits, can't you?" He always winds up his remarks that way. He appears to have an insatiable craving for two bits.

The music struck up just then and saved me. The next moment I was far, far at sea in the plain quadrille. We carried it through with distinguished success; that is, we got as far as "balance around" and "half-a-man-left," when I smelled hot whisky punch, or something of that nature. I tracked the scent through several rooms, and finally discovered a large bowl from which it emanated. I found the omnipresent Unreliable there, also. He set down an empty goblet and remarked that he was diligently seeking the gentlemen's dressing room. I would have shown him where it was, but it occurred to him that the supper table and the punch bowl ought not to be left unprotected; wherefore we stayed there and watched them until the punch entirely evaporated. A servant came in then, to replenish the bowl, and we left the refreshments in his charge. We probably did wrong, but we were anxious to join the hazy dance. The dance was hazier than usual, after that. Sixteen couples on the floor at once, with a few dozen spectators scattered around, is calculated to have its effect in a brilliantly lighted parlor, I believe. Everything seemed to buzz, at any rate. After all the modern dances had been danced several times, the people adjourned to the supper-room. I found my wardrobe out there, as usual, with the Unreliable in it. His old distemper was upon him: he was desperately hungry. I never saw a man eat as much as he did in my life. I have various items of his supper here in my notebook. First, he ate a plate of sandwiches; then he ate a handsomely iced poundcake; then he gobbled a dish of chicken salad; after which he ate a roast pig; after that, a quantity of blanc-mange; then he threw in several dozen glasses of punch to fortify his appetite, and finished his monstrous repast with a roast turkey. Dishes of brandy-grapes, and jellies, and such things, and pyramids of fruits melted away before him as shadows fly at the sun's approach. I am of the opinion that none of his ancestors were present when the five thousand were miraculously fed in the old Scriptural times. I base my opinion on the twelve bushels of scraps and the little fishes that remained over after that feast. If the Unreliable himself had been there, the provisions would just about have held out, I think.

. . . At about two o'clock in the morning the pleasant party broke up and the crowd of guests distributed themselves around town to their respective homes; and after thinking the fun all over again, I went to bed at four o'clock. So having been awake forty-eight hours, I slept forty-eight, in order to get even again.

SAMUEL L. CLEMENS

City Marshal Perry

John Van Buren Perry, recently re-elected City
Marshal of Virginia City, was born a long time ago,
in County Kerry, Ireland, of poor but honest parents,
who were descendants, beyond question, of a house of
high antiquity. The founder of it was distinguished for
his eloquence; he was the property of one Baalam, and
received honorable mention in the Bible.

John Van Buren Perry removed to the United States
in 1792—after having achieved a high gastronomical
reputation by creating the first famine in his native land
—and established himself at Kinderhook, New Jersey,
as a teacher of vocal and instrumental music. His eldest
son, Martin Van Buren, was educated there, and was
afterwards elected President of the United States; his
grandson, of the same name, is now a prominent New
York politician, and is known in the East as "Prince
John;" he keeps up a constant and affectionate corre-
spondence with his worthy grandfather, who sells him
feet in some of his richest wildcat claims from time to
time.

While residing at Kinderhook, Jack Perry was appointed Commodore of the United States Navy, and he
forthwith proceeded to Lake Erie and fought the mighty
marine conflict, which blazes upon the pages of history
as "Perry's Victory." In consequence of this exploit, he
narrowly escaped the Presidency.

Several years ago Commodore Perry was appointed
Commissioner Extraordinary to the Imperial Court of
Japan, with unlimited power to treat. It is hardly worth
while to mention that he never exercised that power; he
never treated anybody in that country, although he patiently submitted to a vast amount of that sort of thing

1809

when the opportunity was afforded him at the expense of the Japanese officials. He returned from his mission full of honors and foreign whisky, and was welcomed home again by the plaudits of a grateful nation.

After the war was ended, Mr. Perry removed to Providence, Rhode Island, where he produced a complete revolution in medical science by inventing the celebrated "Pain Killer" which bears his name. He manufactured this liniment by the ship-load, and spread it far and wide over the suffering world; not a bottle left his establishment without his beneficent portrait upon the label, whereby, in time, his features became as well known unto burned and mutilated children as Jack the Giant Killer's.

When pain had ceased throughout the universe Mr. Perry fell to writing for a livelihood, and for years and years he poured out his soul in pleasing and effeminate poetry. . . . His very first effort, commencing:

> "How doth the little busy bee
> Improve each shining hour," etc.—

gained him a splendid literary reputation, and from that time forward no Sunday-school library was complete without a full edition of his plaintive and sentimental "Perry-Gorics." After great research and profound study of his subject, he produced that wonderful gem which is known in every land as "The Young Mother's Apostrophe to Her Infant," beginning:

> "Fie! fie! oo itty bitty pooty sing!
> To poke oo footsy-tootsys into momma's eye!"

This inspired poem had a tremendous run, and carried Perry's fame into every nursery in the civilized world. But he was not destined to wear his laurels undisturbed: England, with monstrous perfidy, at once claimed the

"Apostrophe" for her favorite son, Martin Farquhar Tupper, and sent up a howl of vindictive abuse from her polluted press against our beloved Perry. With one accord, the American people rose up in his defense, and a devastating war was only averted by a public denial of the paternity of the poem by the great Proverbial over his own signature. This noble act of Mr. Tupper gained him a high place in the affection of this people, and his sweet platitudes have been read here with an ever augmented spirit of tolerance since that day.

The conduct of England toward Mr. Perry told upon his constitution to such an extent that at one time it was feared the gentle bard would fade and flicker out altogether; wherefore, the solicitude of influential officials was aroused in his behalf, and through their generosity he was provided with an asylum in Sing Sing prison, a quiet retreat in the state of New York. Here he wrote his last great poem, beginning:

> "Let dogs delight to bark and bite,
>   For God hath made them so—
> Your little hands were never made
>   To tear out each other's eyes with—"

and then proceeded to learn the shoemaker's trade in his new home, under the distinguished masters employed by the commonwealth.

Ever since Mr. Perry arrived at man's estate his prodigious feet have been a subject of complaint and annoyance to those communities which have known the honor of his presence. In 1835, during a great leather famine, many people were obliged to wear wooden shoes, and Mr. Perry, for the sake of economy, transferred his boot-making patronage from the tan-yard which had before enjoyed his custom, to an undertaker's establishment— that is to say, he wore coffins. At that time he was a member of Congress from New Jersey, and occupied a seat in front of the Speaker's throne. He had the uncouth habit of propping his feet upon his desk during prayer by the chaplain, and thus completely hiding that officer from every eye save that of Omnipotence alone. So long as the Hon. Mr. Perry wore orthodox leather boots the clergyman submitted to this infliction and prayed behind them in singular solitude, under mild protest; but when he arose one morning to offer up his regular petition, and beheld the cheerful apparition of Jack Perry's coffins confronting him, "The jolly old bum went under the table like a sick porpus" (as Mr. P. feelingly remarks), "and never shot off his mouth in that shanty again."

Mr. Perry's first appearance on the Pacific Coast was upon the boards of the San Francisco theaters in the character of "Old Pete" in Dion Boucicault's "Octoroon." So excellent was his delineation of that celebrated character that "Perry's Pete" was for a long time regarded as the climax of histrionic perfection.

Since John Van Buren Perry has resided in Nevada Territory, he has employed his talents in acting as City Marshal of Virginia, and in abusing me because I am an orphan and a long way from home, and can therefore be persecuted with impunity. He was re-elected day before yesterday, and his first official act was an attempt to get me drunk on champagne furnished to the Board of Aldermen by other successful candidates, so that he might achieve the honor and glory of getting me in the stationhouse for once in his life. Although he failed in his object, he followed me down C street and handcuffed me in front of Tom Peasley's, but officers Birdsall and Larkin and Brokaw rebelled against this unwarranted assumption of authority, and released me—whereupon I was about to punish Jack Perry severely, when he offered me six bits to hand him down to posterity through the medium of this Biography, and I closed the contract. But after all, I never expect to get the money.

A SUNDAY IN CARSON

I arrived in this noisy and bustling town of Carson at noon to-day, per Layton's express. We made pretty good time from Virginia, and might have made much better, but for Horace Smith, Esq., who rode on the box seat and kept the stage so much by the head she wouldn't steer. I went to church, of course,—I always go to church when I—when I go to church—as it were. I got there just in time to hear the closing hymn, and also to hear the Rev. Mr. White give out a long-metre doxology, which the choir tried to sing to a short-metre tune. But there wasn't music enough to go around : consequently, the effect was rather singular, than otherwise. They sang the most interesting parts of each line, though, and charged the balance to "profit and loss;" this rendered the general intent and meaning of the doxology considerably mixed, as far as the congregation were concerned, but inasmuch as it was not addressed to them, anyhow, I thought it made no particular difference.

By an easy and pleasant transition, I went from church to jail. It was only just down stairs—for they save men eternally in the second story of the new court house, and damn them for life in the first. Sheriff Gasherie has a handsome double office fronting on the street, and its walls are gorgeously decorated with iron convict-jewelry. In the rear are two rows of cells, built of bomb-proof masonry and furnished with strong iron doors and re-sistless locks and bolts. There was but one prisoner—

Swazey, the murderer of Derrickson—and he was writing; I do not know what his subject was, but he appeared to be handling it in a way which gave him great satisfaction. . . .

ADVICE TO THE UNRELIABLE ON CHURCH-GOING

In the first place, I must impress upon you that when you are dressing for church, as a general thing, you mix your perfumes too much; your fragrance is sometimes oppressive; you saturate yourself with cologne and bergamot, until you make a sort of Hamlet's Ghost of yourself, and no man can decide, with the first whiff, whether you bring with you air from Heaven or from hell. Now, rectify this matter as soon as possible; last Sunday you smelled like a secretary to a consolidated drug store and barber shop. And you came and sat in the same pew with me; now don't do that again.

In the next place when you design coming to church, don't lie in bed until half past ten o'clock and then come in looking all swelled and torpid, like a doughnut. Do reflect upon it, and show some respect for your personal appearance hereafter.

There is another matter, also, which I wish to remonstrate with you about. Generally, when the contribution box of the missionary department is passing around, you begin to look anxious, and fumble in your vest pockets, as if you felt a mighty desire to put all your worldly wealth into it—yet when it reaches your pew, you are sure to be absorbed in your prayer-book, or gazing pensively out of the window at far-off mountains, or buried in meditation, with your sinful head supported by the back of the pew before you. And after the box is gone again, you usually start suddenly and gaze after it with a yearning look, mingled with an expression of bitter disappointment (fumbling your cash again meantime), as if you felt you had missed the one grand opportunity for which you had been longing all your life. Now, to do this when you have money in your pockets is mean. But I have seen you do a meaner thing. I refer to your conduct last Sunday, when the contribution box arrived at our pew—and the angry blood rises to my cheek when I remember with what gravity and sweet serenity of countenance you put in fifty cents and took out two dollars and a half. . . .

THE UNRELIABLE

EDS. ENTERPRISE—I received the following atrocious document the morning I arrived here. It was from that abandoned profligate, the Unreliable, and I think it speaks for itself:

CARSON CITY, Thursday Morning.

To the Unreliable:

SIR—Observing the driver of the Virginia stage hunting after you this morning, in order to collect his fare, I infer you are in town.

In the paper which you represent, I noticed an article which I took to be an effusion from your muddled brain, stating that I had "cabbaged" a number of valuable articles from you the night I took you out of the streets of Washoe City and permitted you to occupy my bed.

I take this opportunity to inform you that I will compensate you at the rate of $20 *per head* for every one of these *valuable* articles that I received from you, providing you will relieve me of their presence. This offer can be either accepted or rejected on your part: but providing you don't see proper to accept it, you had better procure enough lumber to make a box 4x8, and have it made

as early as possible. Judge Dixon will arrange the pre-
liminaries if you don't accede. An early reply is expected
by   RELIABLE.

Not satisfied with wounding my feelings by making
the most extraordinary reference to allusions in the above
note, he even sent a challenge to fight, in the same envelop
with it, hoping to work upon my fears and drive me from
the country by intimidation. But I was not to be frightened; I shall remain in the Territory. I guessed his object at once, and determined to accept his challenge,
choose weapons and things, and scare him, instead of being scared myself. I wrote a stern reply to him, and offered him mortal combat with boot-jacks at a hundred
yards. The effect was more agreeable than I could have
hoped for. His hair turned black in a single night, from
excess of fear; then he went into a fit of melancholy, and
while it lasted he did nothing but sigh, and sob, and
snuffle, and slobber, and say "he wished he was in the
quiet tomb;" finally he said he would commit suicide—
he would say farewell to the cold, cold world, with its
cares and troubles, and go to sleep with his fathers, in
perdition. Then rose up this young man, and threw his
demijohn out of the window, and took up a glass of pure
water, and drained it to the dregs. And then he fell to
the floor in a swoon. Dr. Tjader was called in, and as
soon as he found that the cuss was poisoned, he rushed
down to the Magnolia Saloon and got the antidote, and
poured it down him. As he was drawing his last breath,
he scented the brandy and lingered yet a while on earth,
to take a drink with the boys. But for this he would have
been no more—or possible a great deal less—in a moment. So he survived; but he has been in a mighty pre-
carious condition ever since. I have been up to see how

he was getting along two or three times a day. . . . He
is a very sick man; I was up there a while ago, and I
could see that his friends had begun to entertain hopes
that he would not get over it. As soon as I saw that, all
my enmity vanished; I even felt like doing the poor Unreliable a kindness, and showing him, too, how my feelings toward him had changed. So I went and bought
him a beautiful coffin, and carried it up and set it down
on his bed and told him to climb in when his time was up.
Well, sir, you never saw a man so affected by a little act
of kindness as he was by that. He let off a sort of war-
whoop, and went to kicking things around like a crazy
man; and he foamed at the mouth and went out of one
fit into another faster than I could take them down in my
note-book. . . .

I did not return to Virginia yesterday, on account of
the wedding. The parties were Hon. James H. Sturte-
vant, one of the first Pi-Utes of Nevada, and Miss Emma
Curry, daughter of the Hon. A. Curry, who also claims
that his is a Pi-Ute family of high antiquity. . . . I
had heard it reported that a marriage was threatened, so
felt it my duty to go down there and find out the facts of
the case. They said I might stay, as it was me. . . . I
promised not to say anything about the wedding, and I
regard that promise as sacred—my word is as good as my
bond. . . . Father Bennett advanced and touched off
the high contracting parties with the hymeneal torch
(married them, you know), and at the word of command
from Curry, the fiddle bows were set in motion, and the
plain quadrilles turned loose. Thereupon, some of the
most responsible dancing ensued that I ever saw in my
life. The dance that Tam O'Shanter witnessed was slow
in comparison to it. They kept it up for six hours, and
then carried out the exhausted musicians on a shutter, and

went down to supper. I know they had a fine supper, and plenty of it, but I do not know much else. They drank so much shampin around me that I got confused, and lost the hang of things, as it were. . . . It was mighty pleasant, jolly and sociable, and I wish to thunder I was married myself. I took a large slice of bridal cake home with me to dream on, and dreamt that I was still a single man, and likely to remain so, if I live and nothing happens— which has given me a greater confidence in dreams than I ever felt before. I cordially wish my newly-married couple all kinds of happiness and prosperity, though.

YE SENTIMENTAL LAW STUDENT

EDS. ENTERPRISE—I found the following letter, or Valentine, or whatever it is, lying on the summit, where it had been dropped unintentionally, I think. It was written on a sheet of legal cap, and each line was duly commenced within the red mark which traversed the sheet from top to bottom. Solon appeared to have had some trouble getting his effusion started to suit him. He had begun it, "Know all men by these presents," and scratched it out again; he had substituted, "Now at this day comes the plaintiff, by his attorney," and scratched that out also; he had tried other sentences of like character, and gone on obliterating them, until, through much sorrow and tribulation, he achieved the dedication which stands at the head of his letter, and to his entire satisfaction, I do cheerfully hope. But what a villain a man must be to blend together the beautiful language of love and the infernal phraseology of the law in one and the same sentence! I know but one of God's creatures who would be guilty of such depravity as this: I refer to the Unreliable. I believe the Unreliable to be the very lawyer's-cub who

sat upon the solitary peak, all soaked in beer and senti-
ment, and concocted the insipid literary hash I am talking
about. The handwriting closely resembles his semi-Chi-
nese tarantula tracks.

SUGAR LOAF PEAK, February 14, 1863.
To the loveliness to whom these presents shall come,
greeting:—This is a lovely day, my own Mary; its un-
encumbered sunshine reminds me of your happy face, and
in the imagination the same doth now appear before me.
Such sights and scenes as this ever remind me, the party
of the second part, of you, my Mary, the peerless party of
the first part. The view from the lonely and segregated
mountain peak, of this portion of what is called and
known as Creation, with all and singular the heredita-
ments and appurtenances thereunto appertaining and be-
longing, is inexpressively grand and inspiring; and I
gaze, and gaze, while my soul is filled with holy delight,
and my heart expands to receive thy spirit-presence, as
aforesaid. Above me is the glory of the sun; around him
float the messenger clouds, ready alike to bless the earth
with gentle rain, or visit it with lightning, and thunder,
and destruction; far below the said sun and the messenger
clouds aforesaid, lying prone upon the earth in the verge
of the distant horizon, like the burnished shield of a giant,
mine eyes behold a lake, which is described and set forth
in maps as the Sink of Carson; nearer, in the great plain,
I see the Desert, spread abroad like the mantle of a Colos-
sus, glowing by turns, with the warm light of the sun,
hereinbefore mentioned, or darkly shaded by the messenger clouds aforesaid; flowing at right angles with said
Desert, and adjacent thereto, I see the silver and sinuous
thread of the river, commonly called Carson, which winds
its tortuous course through the softly tinted valley, and

disappears amid the gorges of the bleak and snowy mountains—a simile of man!—leaving the pleasant valley of Peace and Virtue to wander among the dark defiles of Sin, beyond the jurisdiction of the kindly beaming sun aforesaid! And about said sun, and the said clouds, and around the said mountains, and over the plain and the river aforesaid, there floats a purple glory—a yellow mist —as airy and beautiful as the bridal veil of a princess, about to be wedded according to the rites and ceremonies pertaining to, and established by, the laws or edicts of the kingdom or principality wherein she doth reside, and whereof she hath been and doth continue to be, a lawful sovereign or subject. Ah! my Mary, it is sublime! it is lovely! I have declared and made known, and by these presents do declare and make known unto you, that the view from Sugar Loaf Peak, as hereinbefore described and set forth, is the loveliest picture with which the hand of the Creator has adorned the earth, according to the best of my knowledge and belief, so help me God.

Given under my hand, and in the spirit-presence of the bright being whose love has restored the light of hope to a soul once groping in the darkness of despair, on the day and year first above written.

(Signed)   SOLON LYCURGUS.

Law Student, and Notary Public in and for the said County of Storey, and Territory of Nevada.

To Miss Mary Links, Virginia (and may the laws have her in their holy keeping).

SETTIN' BY THE FIRE

BY FRANK L. STANTON

Never much on stirrin' roun'
  (Sich warn't his desire),
Allers certain to be foun'
  Settin' by the fire.

When the frost wuz comin' down—
  Col' win' creepin' nigher,
Spent each day jest thataway—
  Settin' by the fire.

When the dancin' shook the groun'—
  Raised the ol' roof higher,
Never swung the gals eroun'—
  Sot thar' by the fire.

Same ol' corner night an' day—
  Never 'peared to tire;
Not a blessed word to say!
  Jest sot by the fire.

When he died, by slow degrees,
  Folks said: "He's gone higher;"
But it's my opinion he's
  Settin' by the fire.

THE WHISPERER

BY IRONQUILL

He never tried to make a speech;
A speech was far beyond his reach.
　He didn't even dare to try;
　He did his work upon the sly.
　　He took the voter to the rear
　　And gently whispered in his ear.

He never wrote; he could not write;
He never tried that style of fight.
　No argument of his was seen
　In daily press or magazine.
　　He only tried to get up near
　　And whisper in the voter's ear.

It worked so well that he became
A person of abundant fame.
　He couldn't write; he couldn't speak,
　But still pursued his course unique.
　　He had a glorious career—
　　He whispered in the voter's ear.

DER OAK UND DER VINE

BY CHARLES FOLLEN ADAMS

I don'd vas preaching voman's righdts,
    Or anyding like dot,
Und I likes to see all beoples
    Shust gondented mit dheir lot;
Budt I vants to gondradict dot shap
    Dot made dis leedle shoke:
"A voman vas der glinging vine,
    Und man, der shturdy oak."

Berhaps, somedimes, dot may be drue;
    Budt, den dimes oudt off nine,
I find me oudt dot man himself
    Vas peen der glinging vine;
Und ven hees friendts dhey all vas gone,
    Und he vas shust "tead proke,"
Dot's ven der voman shteps righdt in,
    Und peen der shturdy oak.

Shust go oup to der paseball groundts
    Und see dhose "shturdy oaks"
All planted roundt ubon der seats—
    Shust hear dheir laughs und shokes!
Dhen see dhose vomens at der tubs,
    Mit glothes oudt on der lines;
Vhich vas der shturdy oaks, mine friendts,
    Und vhich der glinging vines?

1823

Vhen sickness in der householdt comes,
  Und veeks und veeks he shtays,
Who vas id fighdts him mitoudt resdt,
  Dhose veary nighdts und days?
Who beace und gomfort alvays prings,
  Und cools dot fefered prow?
More like id vas der tender vine
  Dot oak he glings to, now.

"Man vants budt leedle here below,"
  Der boet von time said;
Dhere's leedle dot man he *don'd* vant,
  I dink id means, inshted;
Und ven der years keep rolling on,
  Dheir cares und droubles pringing,
He vants to pe der shturdy oak,
  Und, also, do der glinging.

Maype, vhen oaks dhey gling some more,
  Und don'd so shturdy peen,
Der glinging vines dhey haf some shance
  To helb run Life's masheen.
In helt und sickness, shoy und pain,
  In calm or shtormy veddher,
'T was beddher dot dhose oaks und vines
  Should alvays gling togeddher.

ARAMINTA AND THE AUTOMOBILE

BY CHARLES BATTELL LOOMIS

Some persons spend their surplus on works of art; some spend it on Italian gardens and pergolas; there are those who sink it in golf, and I have heard of those who expended it on charity.

None of these forms of getting away with money appeal to Araminta and myself. As soon as it was ascertained that the automobile was practicable and would not cost a king's ransom, I determined to devote my savings to the purchase of one.

Araminta and I lived in a suburban town; she because she loves Nature and I because I love Araminta. We have been married for five years.

I am a bank clerk in New York, and morning and night I go through the monotony of railway travel, and for one who is forbidden to use his eyes on the train and who does not play cards it *is* monotony, for in the morning my friends are either playing cards or else reading their papers, and one does not like to urge the claims of conversation on one who is deep in politics or the next play of his antagonist; so my getting to business and coming back are in the nature of purgatory. I therefore hailed the automobile as a Heaven-sent means of swift motion with an agreeable companion, and with no danger of encountering either newspapers or cards. I have seen neither reading nor card-playing going on in any automobile.

1825

ARAMINTA AND THE AUTOMOBILE

The community in which I live is not progressive, and when I said that I expected to buy an automobile as soon as my ship came in I was frowned upon by my neighbors. Several of them have horses, and all, or nearly all, have feet. The horsemen were not more opposed to my proposed ownership than the footmen—I should say pedestrians. They all thought automobiles dangerous and a menace to public peace, but of course I pooh-poohed their fears and, being a person of a good deal of stability of purpose, I went on saving my money, and in course of time I bought an automobile of the electric sort.

Araminta is plucky, and I am perfectly fearless. When the automobile was brought home and housed in the little barn that is on our property, the man who had backed it in told me that he had orders to stay and show me how it worked, but I laughed at him—good-naturedly yet firmly. I said, "Young man, experience teaches more in half an hour than books or precepts do in a year. A would-be newspaper man does not go to a school of journalism if he is wise; he gets a position on a newspaper and learns for himself, and through his mistakes. I know that one of these levers is to steer by, that another lets loose the power, and that there is a foot-brake. I also know that the machine is charged, and I need to know no more. Good day."

Thus did I speak to the young man, and he saw that I was a person of force and discretion, and he withdrew to the train and I never saw him again.

Araminta had been to Passaic shopping, but she came back while I was out in the barn looking at my new purchase, and she joined me there. I looked at her lovingly, and she returned the look. Our joint ambition was realized; we were the owners of an automobile, and we were going out that afternoon.

Why is it that cheap barns are so flimsily built? I know that our barn is cheap because the rent for house and barn is less than what many a clerk, city pent, pays for a cramped flat, but again I ask, why are they flimsily built? I have no complaint to make. If my barn had been built of good stout oak I might to-day be in a hospital.

It happened this way. Araminta said, "Let me get in, and we will take just a little ride to see how it goes," and I out of my love for her said, "Wait just a few minutes, dearest, until I get the hang of the thing. I want to see how much go she has and just how she works."

Araminta has learned to obey my slightest word, knowing that love is at the bottom of all my commands, and she stepped to one side while I entered the gayly-painted vehicle and tried to move out of the barn. I moved out. But I backed. Oh, blessed, cheaply built barn. My way was not restricted to any appreciable extent. I shot gayly through the barn into the hen yard, and the sound of the ripping clapboards frightened the silly hens who were enjoying a dust-bath, and they fled in more directions than there were fowls.

I had not intended entering the hen yard, and I did not wish to stay there, so I kept on out, the wire netting not being what an automobile would call an obstruction. I never lose my head, and when I heard Araminta screaming in the barn, I called out cheerily to her, "I'll be back in a minute, dear, but I'm coming another way."

And I did come another way. I came all sorts of ways. I really don't know what got into the machine, but she now turned to the left and made for the road, and then she ran along on her two left wheels for a moment, and then seemed about to turn a somersault, but changed her mind, and, still veering to the left, kept on up the road, passing my house at a furious speed, and making for the open country. With as much calmness as I could summon I steered her, but I think I steered her a little too much, for she turned toward my house.

I reached one end of the front piazza at the same time that Araminta reached the other end of it. I had the right of way, and she deferred to me just in time. I removed the vestibule storm door. It was late in March, and I did not think we should have any more use for it that season. And we didn't.

I had ordered a strongly-built machine, and I was now glad of it, because a light and weak affair that was merely meant to run along on a level and unobstructed road would not have stood the assault on my piazza. Why, my piazza did not stand it. It caved in, and made work for an already overworked local carpenter who was behind-hand with his orders. After I had passed through the vestibule, I applied the brake, and it worked. The path is not a cinder one, as I think them untidy, so I was not more than muddied. I was up in an instant, and looked at the still enthusiastic machine with admiration.

"Have you got the hang of it?" said Araminta.

Now that's one thing I like about Araminta. She does not waste words over non-essentials. The point was not that I had damaged the piazza. I needed a new one, anyway. The main thing was that I was trying to get the hang of the machine, and she recognized that fact instantly.

I told her that I thought I had, and that if I had pushed the lever in the right way at first, I should have come out of the barn in a more conventional way.

She again asked me to let her ride, and as I now felt that I could better cope with the curves of the machine I allowed her to get in.

"Don't lose your head," said I.

"I hope I shan't," said she dryly.

"Well, if you have occasion to leave me, drop over the back. Never jump ahead. That is a fundamental rule in runaways of all kinds."

Then we started, and I ran the motor along for upward of half a mile after I had reached the highway, which I did by a short cut through a field at the side of our house. There is only a slight rail fence surrounding it, and my machine made little of that. It really seemed to delight in what some people would have called danger.

"Araminta, are you glad that I saved up for this?"

"I am mad with joy," said the dear thing, her face flushed with excitement mixed with expectancy. Nor were her expectations to be disappointed. We still had a good deal to do before we should have ended our first ride.

So far I had damaged property to a certain extent, but I had no one but myself to reckon with, and I was providing work for people. I always have claimed that he who makes work for two men where there was only work for one before, is a public benefactor, and that day I was the friend of carpenters and other mechanics.

Along the highway we flew, our hearts beating high, but never in our mouths, and at last we saw a team approaching us. By "a team" I mean a horse and buggy. I was raised in Connecticut, where a team is anything you choose to call one.

The teamster saw us. Well, perhaps I should not call him a teamster (although he was one logically) : he was our doctor, and, as I say, he saw us.

Now I think it would have been friendly in him, seeing that I was more or less of a novice at the art of automobiling, to have turned to the left when he saw that I was inadvertently turning to the left, but the practice of forty years added to a certain native obstinacy made him turn to the right, and he met me at the same time that I met him.

The horse was not hurt, for which I am truly glad, and the doctor joined us, and continued with us for a season, but his buggy was demolished.

Of course I am always prepared to pay for my pleasure, and though it was not, strictly speaking, my pleasure to deprive my physician of his turn-out, yet if he *had* turned out it wouldn't have happened—and, as I say, I was prepared to get him a new vehicle. But he was very unreasonable; so much so that, as he was crowding us—for the seat was not built for more than two, and he is stout— I at last told him that I intended to turn around and carry him home, as we were out for pleasure, and he was giving us pain.

I will confess that the events of the last few minutes had rattled me somewhat, and I did not feel like turning just then, as the road was narrow. I knew that the road turned of its own accord a half-mile farther on, and so I determined to wait.

"I want to get out," said the doctor tartly, and just as he said so Araminta stepped on the brake, accidentally. The doctor got out—in front. With great presence of mind I reversed, and so we did not run over him. But he was furious and sulphurous, and that is why I have changed to homeopathy. He was the only allopathic doctor in Brantford.

I suppose that if I had stopped and apologized, he would have made up with me, and I would not have got angry with him, but I couldn't stop. The machine was now going as she had done when I left the barn, and we were backing into town.

Through it all I did not lose my coolness. I said:

"Araminta, look out behind, which is ahead of us, and if you have occasion to jump now, do it in front, which is behind," and Araminta understood me.

She sat sideways, so that she could see what was going on, but that might have been seen from any point of view, for we were the only things going on—or backing.

Pretty soon we passed the wreck of the buggy, and then we saw the horse grazing on dead grass by the roadside, and at last we came on a few of our townfolk who had seen us start, and were now come out to welcome us home. But I did not go home just then. I should have done so if the machine had minded me and turned in at our driveway, but it did not.

Across the way from us there is a fine lawn leading up to a beautiful greenhouse full of rare orchids and other plants. It is the pride of my very good neighbor, Jacob Rawlinson.

The machine, as if moved by *malice prépense,* turned just as we came to the lawn, and began to back at railroad speed.

I told Araminta that if she was tired of riding, now was the best time to stop; that she ought not to overdo it, and that I was going to get out myself as soon as I had seen her off.

I saw her off.

Then after one ineffectual jab at the brake, I left the machine hurriedly, and as I sat down on the sposhy lawn I heard a tremendous but not unmusical sound of falling glass—

I tell Araminta that it isn't the running of an automobile that is expensive. It is the stopping of it.

THE HEIGHT OF THE RIDICULOUS

BY OLIVER WENDELL HOLMES

I wrote some lines once on a time
  In wondrous merry mood,
And thought, as usual, men would say
  They were exceeding good.

They were so queer, so very queer,
  I laughed as I would die;
Albeit, in the general way,
  A sober man am I.

I called my servant, and he came;
  How kind it was of him
To mind a slender man like me,
  He of the mighty limb!

"These to the printer," I exclaimed,
  And, in my humorous way,
I added, (as a trifling jest,)
  "There'll be the devil to pay."

He took the paper, and I watched,
  And saw him peep within;
At the first line he read, his face
  Was all upon the grin.

He read the next; the grin grew broad,
  And shot from ear to ear;
He read the third; a chuckling noise
  I now began to hear.

1832

The fourth; he broke into a roar;
 The fifth; his waistband split;
The sixth; he burst five buttons off,
 And tumbled in a fit.

Ten days and nights, with sleepless eye,
 I watched that wretched man,
And since, I never dare to write
 As funny as I can.

1833

WHEN LOVELY WOMAN

BY PHŒBE CARY

When lovely woman wants a favor,
   And finds, too late, that man won't bend,
What earthly circumstance can save her
   From disappointment in the end?

The only way to bring him over,
   The last experiment to try,
Whether a husband or a lover,
   If he have feeling is—to cry.

1834

UNSATISFIED YEARNING

BY R. K. MUNKITTRICK

Down in the silent hallway
   Scampers the dog about,
And whines, and barks, and scratches,
   In order to get out.

Once in the glittering starlight,
   He straightway doth begin
To set up a doleful howling
   In order to get in.

THE INVISIBLE PRINCE*

BY HENRY HARLAND

At a masked ball given by the Countess Wohenhoffen, in Vienna, during carnival week, a year ago, a man draped in the embroidered silks of a Chinese mandarin, his features entirely concealed by an enormous Chinese head in cardboard, was standing in the Wintergarten, the big, dimly-lighted conservatory, near the door of one of the gilt-and-white reception-rooms, rather a stolid-seeming witness of the multi-coloured romp within, when a voice behind him said, "How do you do, Mr. Field?" —a woman's voice, an English voice.

The mandarin turned round.

From a black mask, a pair of blue-gray eyes looked into his broad, bland Chinese face; and a black domino dropped him an extravagant little curtsey.

"How do you do?" he responded. "I'm afraid I'm not Mr. Field; but I'll gladly pretend I am, if you'll stop and talk with me. I was dying for a little human conversation."

"Oh you're afraid you're not Mr. Field, are you?" the mask replied derisively. "Then why did you turn when I called his name?"

"You mustn't hope to disconcert me with questions like that," said he. "I turned because I liked your voice."

He might quite reasonably have liked her voice, a delicate, clear, soft voice, somewhat high in register, with an accent, crisp, chiselled, concise, that suggested wit as well

---

*From *Comedies and Errors*. Reprinted by permission of the John Lane Company.

1836

as distinction. She was rather tall, for a woman; one could divine her slender and graceful, under the voluminous folds of her domino.

She moved a little away from the door, deeper into the conservatory. The mandarin kept beside her. There, amongst the palms, a *fontaine lumineuse* was playing, rhythmically changing colour. Now it was a shower of rubies; now of emeralds or amethysts, of sapphires, topazes, or opals.

"How pretty," she said, "and how frightfully ingenious. I am wondering whether this wouldn't be a good place to sit down. What do *you* think?" And she pointed with a fan to a rustic bench.

So they sat down on the rustic bench, by the *fontaine lumineuse*.

"In view of your fear that you're not Mr. Field, it's rather a coincidence that at a masked ball in Vienna you should just happen to be English, isn't it?" she asked.

"Oh, everybody's more or less English, in these days, you know," said he.

"There's some truth in that," she admitted, with a laugh. "What a diverting piece of artifice this Wintergarten is, to be sure. Fancy arranging the electric lights to shine through a dome of purple glass, and look like stars. They do look like stars, don't they? Slightly overdressed, showy stars, indeed; stars in the German taste; but stars, all the same. Then, by day, you know, the purple glass is removed, and you get the sun—the real sun. Do you notice the delicious fragrance of lilac? If one hadn't too exacting an imagination, one might almost persuade oneself that one was in a proper open-air garden, on a night in May— Yes, everybody is more or less English, in these days. That's precisely the sort of thing I should have expected Victor Field to say."

"By-the-bye," questioned the mandarin, "if you don't mind increasing my stores of knowledge, who *is* this fellow Field?"

"This fellow Field? Ah, who indeed?" said she. "That's just what I wish you'd tell me."

"I'll tell you with pleasure, after you've supplied me with the necessary data," he promised cheerfully.

"Well, by some accounts, he's a little literary man in London," she remarked.

"Oh, come! You never imagined that I was a little literary man in London," protested he.

"You might be worse," she retorted. "However, if the phrase offends you, I'll say a rising young literary man, instead. He writes things, you know."

"Poor chap, does he? But then, that's a way they have, sizing up literary persons?" His tone was interrogative.

"Doubtless," she agreed. "Poems and stories and things. And book reviews, I suspect. And even, perhaps, leading articles in the newspapers."

"*Toute la lyre enfin?* What they call a penny-a-liner?"

"I'm sure I don't know what he's paid. I should think he'd get rather more than a penny. He's fairly successful. The things he does aren't bad," she said.

"I must look 'em up," said he. "But meantime, will you tell me how you came to mistake me for him?" Has he the Chinese type? Besides, what on earth should a little London literary man be doing at the Countess Wohenhoffen's?"

"He was standing near the door, over there," she told him, sweetly, "dying for a little human conversation, till I took pity on him. No, he hasn't exactly the Chinese type, but he's wearing a Chinese costume, and I should suppose he'd feel uncommonly hot in that exasperatingly placid Chinese head. *I'm* nearly suffocated, and I'm only wearing a *loup*. For the rest, why *shouldn't* he be here?"

"If your *loup* bothers you, pray take it off. Don't mind me," he urged gallantly.

"You're extremely good," she responded. "But if I should take off my *loup,* you'd be sorry. Of course, manlike, you're hoping that I'm young and pretty."

"Well, and aren't you?"

"I'm a perfect fright. I'm an old maid."

"Thank you. Manlike, I confess I *was* hoping you'd be young and pretty. Now my hope has received the strongest confirmation. I'm sure you are," he declared triumphantly.

"Your argument, with a meretricious air of subtlety, is facile and superficial. Don't pin your faith to it. Why *shouldn't* Victor Field be here?" she persisted.

"The Countess only receives tremendous swells. It's the most exclusive house in Europe."

"Are you a tremendous swell?" she wondered.

"Rather!" he asseverated. "Aren't you?"

She laughed a little, and stroked her fan, a big fan, a big fan of fluffy black feathers.

"That's very jolly," said he.

"What?" said she.

"That thing in your lap."

"My fan?"

"I expect you'd call it a fan."

"For goodness' sake, what would *you* call it?" cried she.

"I should call it a fan."

She gave another little laugh. "You have a nice instinct for the *mot juste,*" she informed him.

"Oh, no," he disclaimed, modestly. "But I can call a

fan a fan, when I think it won't shock the sensibilities of my hearer."

"If the Countess only receives tremendous swells," said she, "you must remember that Victor Field belongs to the Aristocracy of Talent."

"Oh, *quant à ça*, so, from the Wohenhoffens' point of view, do the barber and the horse-leech. In this house, the Aristocracy of Talent dines with the butler."

"Is the Countess such a snob?" she asked.

"No; she's an Austrian. They draw the line so absurdly tight in Austria."

"Well, then, you leave me no alternative," she argued, "but to conclude that Victor Field is a tremendous swell. Didn't you notice, I bobbed him a curtsey?"

"I took the curtsey as a tribute to my Oriental magnificence," he confessed. "Field doesn't sound like an especially patrician name. I'd give anything to discover who you are. Can't you be induced to tell me? I'll bribe, entreat, threaten—I'll do anything you think might persuade you."

"I'll tell you at once, if you'll own up that you're Victor Field," said she.

"Oh, I'll own up that I'm Queen Elizabeth if you'll tell me who you are. The end justifies the means."

"Then you *are* Victor Field?" she pursued him eagerly.

"If you don't mind suborning perjury, why should I mind committing it?" he reflected. "Yes. And now, who are you?"

"No; I must have an unequivocal avowal," she stipulated. "Are you or are you not Victor Field?"

"Let us put it at this," he proposed, "that I'm a good serviceable imitation; an excellent substitute when the genuine article is not procurable."

"Of course, your real name isn't anything like Victor Field," she declared, pensively.

"I never said it was. But I admire the way in which you give with one hand and take back with the other."

"Your real name—" she began. "Wait a moment— Yes, now I have it. Your real name— It's rather long. You don't think it will bore you?"

"Oh, if it's really my real name, I daresay I'm hardened to it," said he.

"Your real name is Louis Charles Ferdinand Stanislas John Joseph Emmanuel Maria Anna."

"Mercy upon me," he cried, "what a name! You ought to have broken it to me in instalments. And it's all Christian name at that. Can't you spare me just a little rag of a surname, for decency's sake?" he pleaded.

"The surnames of royalties don't matter, Monseigneur," she said, with a flourish.

"Royalties? What? Dear me, here's rapid promotion! I am royal now! And a moment ago I was a little penny-a-liner in London."

"*L'un n'empêche pas l'autre.* Have you never heard the story of the Invisible Prince?" she asked.

"I adore irrelevancy," said he. "I seem to have read something about an invisible prince, when I was young. A fairy tale, wasn't it?"

"The irrelevancy is only apparent. The story I mean is a story of real life. Have you ever heard of the Duke of Zeln?"

"Zeln? Zeln?" he repeated, reflectively. "No, I don't think so."

She clapped her hands. "Really, you do it admirably. If I weren't perfectly sure of my facts, I believe I should be taken in. Zeln, as any history would tell you, as any old atlas would show you, was a little independent duchy in the center of Germany."

"Poor dear thing! Like Jonah in the center of the whale," he murmured, sympathetically.

"Hush. Don't interrupt. Zeln was a little independent German duchy, and the Duke of Zeln was its sovereign. After the war with France it was absorbed by Prussia. But the ducal family still rank as royal highness. Of course, you've heard of the Leczinskis?"

"Lecz—what?" said he.

"Leczinski," she repeated.

"How do you spell it?"

"L-e-c-z-i-n-s-k-i."

"Good. Capital. You have a real gift for spelling," he exclaimed.

"Will you be quiet," she said, severely, "and answer my question? Are you familiar with the name?"

"I should never venture to be familiar with a name I didn't know," he asserted.

"Ah, you don't know it? You have never heard of Stanislas Leczinska, who was king of Poland? Of Marie Leczinska, who married Louis VI?"

"Oh, to be sure. I remember. The lady whose portrait one sees at Versailles."

"Quite so. Very well," she continued, "the last representative of the Leczinskis, in the elder line, was the Princess Anna Leczinska, who, in 1858, married the Duke of Zeln. She was the daughter of John Leczinski, Duke of Grodnia and Governor of Galicia, and of the Archduchess Henrietta d'Este, a cousin of the Emperor of Austria. She was also a great heiress, and an extremely handsome woman. But the Duke of Zeln was a bad lot, a viveur, a gambler, a spendthrift. His wife, like a fool, made her entire fortune over to him, and he

proceeded to play ducks and drakes with it. By the time
their son was born he'd got rid of the last farthing. Their
son wasn't born till '63, five years after their marriage.
Well, and then, what do you suppose the Duke did?"

"Reformed, of course. The wicked husband always
reforms when a child is born, and there's no more
money," he generalized.

"You know perfectly well what he did," said she. "He
petitioned the German Diet to annul the marriage. You
see, having exhausted the dowry of the Princess Anna,
it occurred to him that if she could only be got out of the
way, he might marry another heiress, and have the spend-
ing of another fortune."

"Clever dodge," he observed. "Did it come off?"

"It came off, all too well. He based his petition on the
ground that the marriage had never been— I forget what
the technical term is. Anyhow, he pretended that the
princess had never been his wife except in name, and that
the child couldn't possibly be his. The Emperor of Austria stood by his connection, like the royal gentleman he
is; used every scrap of influence he possessed to help her.
But the duke, who was a Protestant (the princess was
of course a Catholic), the duke persuaded all the Protestant States in the Diet to vote in his favour. The Emperor
of Austria was powerless, the Pope was powerless. And
the Diet annulled the marriage."

"Ah," said the mandarin.

"Yes," she went on. "The marriage was annulled, and
the child declared illegitimate. Ernest Augustus, as the
duke was somewhat inconsequently named, married
again, and had other children, the eldest of whom is the
present bearer of the title—the same Duke of Zeln one
hears of, quarreling with the croupiers at Monte Carlo.
The Princess Anna, with her baby, came to Austria. The

Emperor gave her a pension, and lent her one of his country houses to live in—Schloss Sanct—Andreas. Our hostess, by-the-by, the Countess Wohenhoffen, was her intimate friend and her *première dame d'honneur.*"

"Ah," said the mandarin.

"But the poor princess had suffered more than she could bear. She died when her child was four years old. The Countess Wohenhoffen took the infant, by the Emperor's desire, and brought him up with her own son Peter. He was called Prince Louis Leczinski. Of course, in all moral right, he was the Hereditary Prince of Zeln. His legitimacy, for the rest, and his mother's innocence, are perfectly well established, in every sense but a legal sense, by the fact that he has all the physical characteristics of the Zeln stock. He has the Zeln nose and the Zeln chin, which are as distinctive as the Hapsburg lip."

"I hope, for the poor young man's sake, though, that they're not so unbecoming?" questioned the mandarin.

"They're not exactly pretty," answered the mask. "The nose is a thought too long, the chin is a trifle too short. However, I daresay the poor young man is satisfied. As I was about to tell you, the Countess Wohenhoffen brought him up, and the Emperor destined him for the Church. He even went to Rome and entered the Austrian College. He'd have been on the high road to a cardinalate by this time if he'd stuck to the priesthood, for he had strong interest. But, lo and behold, when he was about twenty, he chucked the whole thing up."

"Ah? *Histoire de femme?*"

"Very likely," she assented, "though I've never heard any one say so. At all events, he left Rome, and started upon his travels. He had no money of his own, but the Emperor made him an allowance. He started upon his travels, and he went to India, and he went to America, and he went to South Africa, and then, finally, in '87 or '88, he went—no one knows where. He totally disappeared, vanished into space. He's not been heard of since. Some people think he's dead. But the greater number suppose that he tired of his false position in the world, and one fine day determined to escape from it, by sinking his identity, changing his name, and going in for a new life under new conditions. They call him the Invisible Prince. His position *was* rather an ambiguous one, wasn't it? You see, he was neither one thing nor the other. He has no *état-civil*. In the eyes of the law he was a bastard, yet he knew himself to be the legitimate son of the Duke of Zeln. He was a citizen of no country, yet he was the rightful heir to a throne. He was the last descendant of Stanislas Leczinski, yet it was without authority that he bore his name. And then, of course, the rights and wrongs of the matter were only known to a few. The majority of people simply remembered that there had been a scandal. And (as a wag once said of him) wherever he went, he left his mother's reputation behind him. No wonder he found the situation irksome. Well, there is the story of the Invisible Prince."

"And a very exciting, melodramatic little story, too. For my part, I suspect your Prince met a boojum. I love to listen to stories. Won't you tell me another? Do, please," he pressed her.

"No, he didn't meet a boojum," she returned. "He went to England, and set up for an author. The Invisible Prince and Victor Field are one and the same person."

"Oh, I say! Not really!" he exclaimed.

"Yes, really."

"What makes you think so?" he wondered.

"I'm sure of it," said she. "To begin with, I must confide to you that Victor Field is a man I've never met."

"Never met—?" he gasped. "But, by the blithe way in which you were laying his sins at my door, a little while ago, I supposed you were sworn confederates."

"What's the good of masked balls, if you can't talk to people you've never met?" she submitted. "I've never met him, but I'm one of his admirers. I like his little poems. And I'm the happy possessor of a portrait of him. It's a print after a photograph. I cut it from an illustrated paper."

"I really almost wish I *was* Victor Field," he sighed. "I should feel such a glow of gratified vanity."

"And the Countess Wohenhoffen," she added, "has at least twenty portraits of the Invisible Prince—photographs, miniatures, life-size paintings, taken from the time he was born, almost, to the time of his disappearance. Victor Field and Louis Leczinski have countenances as like each other as two halfpence."

"An accidental resemblance, doubtless."

"No, it isn't an accidental resemblance," she affirmed.

"Oh, then you think it's intentional?" he quizzed.

"Don't be absurd. I might have thought it accidental, except for one or two odd little circumstances. *Primo,* Victor Field is a guest at the Wohenhoffens' ball."

"Oh, he *is* a guest here?"

"Yes, he is," she said. "You are wondering how I know. Nothing simpler. The same *costumier* who made my domino, supplied his Chinese dress. I noticed it at his shop. It struck me as rather nice, and I asked whom it was for. The *costumier* said, for an Englishman at the Hôtel de Bade. Then he looked in his book, and told me the Englishman's name. It was Victor Field. So, when I saw the same Chinese dress here to-night, I knew it covered the person of one of my favorite authors. But I own, like you, I was a good deal surprised. What on

1846

earth should a little London literary man be doing at the Countess Wohenhoffen's? And then I remembered the astonishing resemblance between Victor Field and Louis Leczinski; and I remembered that to Louis Leczinski the Countess Wohenhoffen had been a second mother; and I reflected that though he chose to be as one dead and buried for the rest of the world, Louis Leczinski might very probably keep up private relations with the Countess. He might very probably come to her ball, incognito, and safely masked. I observed also that the Countess's rooms were decorated throughout with *white lilac*. But the white lilac is the emblematic flower of the Leczinskis; green and white are their family colours. Wasn't the choice of white lilac on this occasion perhaps designed as a secret compliment to the Prince? I was taught in the schoolroom that two and two make four."

"Oh, one can see that you've enjoyed a liberal education," he apprised her. "But where were you taught to jump to conclusions? You do it with a grace, an assurance. I too have heard that two and two make four; but first you must catch your two and two. Really, as if there couldn't be more than one Chinese costume knocking about Vienna, during carnival week! Dear, good, sweet lady, it's of all disguises the disguise they're driving hardest, this particular season. And then to build up an elaborate theory of identities upon the mere chance resemblance of a pair of photographs! Photographs indeed! Photographs don't give the complexion. Say that your Invisible Prince is dark, what's to prevent your literary man from being fair or sandy? Or *vice versâ?* And then, how is a little German Polish princeling to write poems and things in English? No, no, no; your reasoning hasn't a leg to stand on."

"Oh, I don't mind its not having legs," she laughed,

"so long as it convinces me. As for writing poems and things in English, you yourself said that everybody is more or less English, in these days. German princes are especially so. They all learn English, as a second mother-tongue. You see, like Circassian beauties, they are mostly bred up for the marriage market; and nothing is a greater help towards a good sound remunerative English marriage, than a knowledge of the language. However, don't be frightened. I must take it for granted that Victor Field would prefer not to let the world know who he is. I happen to have discovered his secret. He may trust to my discretion."

"You still persist in imagining that I'm Victor Field?" he murmured sadly.

"I should have to be extremely simple-minded," she announced, "to imagine anything else. You wouldn't be a male human being if you had sat here for half an hour patiently talking about another man."

"Your argument," said he, "with a meretricious air of subtlety, is facile and superficial. I thank you for teaching me that word. I'd sit here till doomsday talking about my worst enemy, for the pleasure of talking with you."

"Perhaps we have been talking of your worst enemy. Whom do the moralists pretend a man's worst enemy is wont to be?" she asked.

"I wish you would tell me the name of the person the moralists would consider *your* worst enemy," he replied.

"I'll tell you directly, as I said before, if you'll own up," she offered.

"Your price is prohibitive. I've nothing to own up to."

"Well then—good night," she said.

Lightly, swiftly, she fled from the conservatory, and was soon irrecoverable in the crowd.

The next morning Victor Field left Vienna for London; but before he left he wrote a letter to Peter Wohenhoffen. In the course of it he said: "There was an Englishwoman at your ball last night with the reasoning powers of a detective in a novel. By divers processes of elimination and induction, she had formed all sorts of theories about no end of things. Among others, for instance, she was willing to bet her halidome that a certain Prince Louis Leczinski, who seems to have gone on the spree some years ago, and never to have come home again—she was willing to bet anything you like that Leczinski and I—*moi qui vous parle*—were to all intents and purposes the same. Who was she, please? Rather a tall woman, in a black domino, with gray eyes, or grayish-blue, and a nice voice."

In the answer which he received from Peter Wohenhoffen towards the end of the week, Peter said: "There were nineteen Englishwomen at my mother's party, all of them rather tall, with nice voices, and gray or blue-gray eyes. I don't know what colours their dominoes were. Here is a list of them."

The names that followed were names of people whom Victor Field almost certainly would never meet. The people Victor knew in London were the sort of people a little literary man might be expected to know. Most of them were respectable; some of them even deemed themselves rather smart, and patronized him right Britishly. But the nineteen names in Peter Wohenhoffen's list ("Oh, me! Oh, my!" cried Victor) were names to make you gasp.

All the same, he went a good deal to Hyde Park during the season, and watched the driving.

"Which of all those haughty high-born beauties is she?" he wondered futilely.

THE INVISIBLE PRINCE

And then the season passed, and then the year; and little by little, of course, he ceased to think about her.

One afternoon last May, a man, habited in accordance with the fashion of the period, stopped before a hairdresser's shop in Knightsbridge somewhere, and, raising his hat, bowed to the three waxen ladies who simpered from the window.

"Oh! It's Mr. Field!" a voice behind him cried. "What are those cryptic rites that you're performing? What on earth are you bowing into a hairdresser's window for?"—a smooth, melodious voice, tinged by an inflection that was half ironical, half bewildered.

"I was saluting the type of English beauty," he answered, turning. "Fortunately, there are divergencies from it," he added, as he met the puzzled smile of his interlocutrice; a puzzled smile, indeed, but, like the voice, by no means without its touch of irony.

She gave a little laugh; and then, examining the models critically, "Oh?" she questioned. "Would you call that the type? You place the type high. Their features are quite faultless, and who ever saw such complexions?"

"It's the type, all the same," said he. "Just as the imitation marionette is the type of English breeding."

"The imitation marionette? I'm afraid I don't follow," she confessed.

"The imitation marionettes. You've seen them at little theatres in Italy. They're actors who imitate puppets. Men and women who try to behave as if they weren't human, as if they were made of starch and whalebone, instead of flesh and blood."

"Ah, yes," she assented, with another little laugh. "That *would* be rather typical of our insular methods. But do you know what an engaging, what a reviving spectacle you presented, as you stood there flourishing your hat? What do you imagine people thought? And what would have happened to you if I had just chanced to be a policeman instead of a friend?"

"Would you have clapped your handcuffs on me?" he inquired. "I suppose my conduct did seem rather suspicious. I was in the deepest depths of dejection. One must give some expression to one's sorrow."

"Are you going towards Kensington?" she asked, preparing to move on.

"Before I commit myself, I should like to be sure whether you are," he replied.

"You can easily discover with a little perseverance."

He placed himself beside her, and together they walked towards Kensington.

She was rather taller than the usual woman, and slender. She was exceedingly well-dressed; smartly, becomingly; a jaunty little hat of strangely twisted straw, with an aigrette springing defiantly from it; a jacket covered with mazes and labyrinths of embroidery; at her throat a big knot of white lace, the ends of which fell winding in a creamy cascade to her waist (do they call the thing a *jabot?*); and then . . .   But what can a man trust himself to write of these esoteric matters? She carried herself extremely well, too: with grace, with distinction, her head held high, even thrown back a little, superciliously. She had an immense quantity of very lovely hair. Red hair? Yellow hair? Red hair with yellow lights burning in it? Yellow hair with red fires shimmering through it? In a single loose, full billow it swept away from her forehead, and then flowed into a half-a-thousand rippling, crinkling, capricious undulations. And her skin had the sensitive colouring, the fineness of texture, that are apt to accompany red hair when it's yellow,

yellow hair when it's red. Her face, with its pensive, quizzical eyes, its tip-tilted nose, its rather large mouth, and the little mocking quirks and curves the lips took, with an alert, arch, witty face; a delicate high-bred face; and withal a somewhat sensuous, emotional face; the face of a woman with a vast deal of humour in her soul; a vast deal of mischief; of a woman who would love to tease you, and mystify you, and lead you on, and put you off; and yet who, in her own way, at her own time, would know supremely well how to be kind.

But it was mischief rather than kindness that glimmered in her eyes at present, as she asked, "You were in the deepest depths of dejection? Poor man! Why?"

"I can't precisely determine," said he, "whether the sympathy that seems to vibrate in your voice is genuine or counterfeit."

"Perhaps it's half and half," she suggested. "But my curiosity is unmixed. Tell me your troubles."

"The catalogue is long. I've sixteen hundred million. The weather, for example. The shameless beauty of this radiant spring day. It's enough to stir all manner of wild pangs and longings in the heart of an octogenarian. But, anyhow, when one's life is passed in a dungeon, one can't perpetually be singing and dancing from mere exuberance of joy, can one?"

"Is your life passed in a dungeon?" she exclaimed.

"Indeed, indeed, it is. Isn't yours?"

"It had never occurred to me that it was."

"You're lucky. Mine is passed in the dungeons of Castle Ennui," he said.

"Oh, Castle Ennui. Ah, yes. You mean you're bored?"

"At this particular moment I'm savouring the most exquisite excitement," he professed. "But in general, when I am not working or sleeping, I'm bored to extermination—incomparably bored. If only one could work and sleep alternately, twenty-four hours a day, the year round! There's no use trying to play in London. It's so hard to find a playmate. The English people take their pleasures without salt."

"The dungeons of Castle Ennui," she repeated meditatively. "Yes, we are fellow-prisoners. I'm bored to extermination too. Still," she added, "one is allowed out on parole, now and again. And sometimes one has really quite delightful little experiences."

"It would ill become me, in the present circumstances, to dispute that," he answered, bowing.

"But the castle waits to reclaim us afterwards, doesn't it?" she mused. "That's rather a happy image, Castle Ennui."

"I'm extremely glad you approve of it. Castle Ennui is the bastile of modern life. It is built of prunes and prisms; it has its outer court of convention, and its inner court of propriety; it is moated round by respectability, and the shackles its inmates wear are forged of dull little duties and arbitrary little rules. You can only escape from it at the risk of breaking your social neck, or remaining a fugitive from social justice to the end of your days. Yes, it *is* a fairly decent little image."

"A bit out of something you're preparing for the press?" she hinted.

"Oh, how unkind of you!" he cried. "It was absolutely extemporaneous."

"One can never tell, with *vous autres gens-de-lettres*," she laughed.

"It would be friendlier to say *nous autres gens d'esprit*," he submitted.

"Aren't we proving to what degree *nous autres gens d'esprit sont bêtes*," she remarked, "by continuing to walk along this narrow pavement, when we can get into Kensington Gardens by merely crossing the street. Would it take you out of your way?"

"I have no way. I was sauntering for pleasure, if you can believe me. I wish I could hope that you have no way either. Then we could stop here, and crack little jokes together the livelong afternoon," he said, as they entered the Gardens.

"Alas, my way leads straight back to the Castle. I've promised to call on an old woman in Campden Hill," said she.

"Disappoint her. It's good for old women to be disappointed. It whips up their circulation."

"I shouldn't much regret disappointing the old woman," she admitted, "and I should rather like an hour or two of stolen freedom. I don't mind owning that I've generally found you, as men go, a moderately interesting man to talk with. But the deuce of it is— You permit the expression?"

"I'm devoted to the expression."

"The deuce of it is, I'm supposed to be driving," she explained.

"Oh, that doesn't matter. So many suppositions in this world are baseless," he reminded her.

"But there's the prison van," she said. "It's one of the tiresome rules in the female wing of Castle Ennui that you're always supposed, more or less, to be driving. And though you may cheat the authorities by slipping out of the prison van directly it's turned the corner, and sending it on ahead, there it remains, a factor that can't be eliminated. The prison van will relentlessly await my arrival in the old woman's street."

"That only adds to the sport. Let it wait. When a factor can't be eliminated, it should be haughtily ignored.

Besides, there are higher considerations. If you leave me, what shall I do with the rest of this weary day?"

"You can go to your club."

He threw up his hand. "Merciful lady! What sin have I committed? I never go to my club, except when I've been wicked, as a penance. If you will permit me to employ a metaphor—oh, but a tried and trusty metaphor—when one ship on the sea meets another in distress, it stops and comforts it, and forgets all about its previous engagements and the prison van and everything. Shall we cross to the north, and see whether the Serpentine is in its place? Or would you prefer to inspect the eastern front of the Palace? Or may I offer you a penny chair?"

"I think a penny chair would be the maddest of the three dissipations," she decided.

And they sat down in penny chairs.

"It's rather jolly here, isn't it?" said he. "The trees, with their black trunks, and their leaves, and things. Have you ever seen such sumptuous foliage? And the greensward, and the shadows, and the sunlight, and the atmosphere, and the mistiness—isn't it like pearl-dust and gold-dust floating in the air? It's all got up to imitate the background of a Watteau. We must do our best to be frivolous and ribald, and supply a proper foreground. How big and fleecy and white the clouds are. Do you think they're made of cotton-wood? And what do you suppose they paint the sky with? There never was such a brilliant, breath-taking blue. It's much too nice to be natural. And they've sprinkled the whole place with scent, haven't they? You notice how fresh and sweet it smells. If only one could get rid of the sparrows—the cynical little beasts! hear how they're chortling—and the people, and the nursemaids and children. I have never been able to understand why they admit the public to the parks."

"Go on," she encouraged him. "You're succeeding admirably in your effort to be ribald."

"But that last remark wasn't ribald in the least—it was desperately sincere. I do think it's inconsiderate of them to admit the public to the parks. They ought to exclude all the lower classes, the people, at one fell swoop, and then to discriminate tremendously amongst the others."

"Mercy, what undemocratic sentiments!" she cried. "The People, the poor dear People—what have they done?"

"Everything. What haven't they done? One could forgive their being dirty and stupid and noisy and rude; one could forgive their ugliness, the ineffable banality of their faces, their goggle-eyes, their protruding teeth, their ungainly motions; but the trait one can't forgive is their venality. They're so mercenary. They're always thinking how much they can get out of you—everlastingly touching their hats and expecting you to put your hand in your pocket. Oh, no, believe me, there's no health in the People. Ground down under the iron heel of despotism, reduced to a condition of hopeless serfdom, I don't say that they might not develop redeeming virtues. But free, but sovereign, as they are in these days, they're everything that is squalid and sordid and offensive. Besides, they read such abominably bad literature."

"In that particular they're curiously like the aristocracy, aren't they?" said she. "By-the-bye, when are you going to publish another book of poems?"

"Apropos of bad literature?"

"Not altogether bad. I rather like your poems."

"So do I," said he. "It's useless to pretend that we haven't tastes in common."

They were both silent for a bit. She looked at him oddly, an inscrutable little light flickering in her eyes. All at once she broke out with a merry trill of laughter.

"What are you laughing at?" he demanded.

"I'm hugely amused," she answered.

"I wasn't aware that I'd said anything especially good."

"You're building better than you know. But if I am amused, *you* look ripe for tears. What is the matter?"

"Every heart knows its own bitterness," he answered. "Don't pay the least attention to me. You mustn't let moodiness of mine cast a blight upon your high spirits."

"No fear," she assured him. "There are pleasures that nothing can rob of their sweetness. Life is not all dust and ashes. There are bright spots."

"Yes, I've no doubt there are," he said.

"And thrilling little adventures—no?" she questioned.

"For the bold, I dare say."

"None but the bold deserve them. Sometimes it's one thing, and sometimes it's another."

"That's very certain," he agreed.

"Sometimes, for instance," she went on, "one meets a man one knows, and speaks to him. And he answers with a glibness! And then, almost directly, what do you suppose one discovers?"

"What?" he asked.

"One discovers that the wretch hasn't a ghost of a notion who one is—that he's totally and absolutely forgotten one!"

"Oh, I say! Really?" he exclaimed.

"Yes, really. You can't deny that *that's* an exhilarating little adventure."

"I should think it might be. One could enjoy the man's embarrassment," he reflected.

1857

"Or his lack of embarrassment. Some men are of an assurance, of a *sang froid!* They'll place themselves beside you, and walk with you, and talk with you, and even propose that you should pass the livelong afternoon cracking jokes with them in a garden, and never breathe a hint of their perplexity. They'll brazen it out."

"That's distinctly heroic, Spartan, of them, don't you think?" he said. "Intentionally, poor dears, they're very likely suffering agonies of discomfiture."

"We'll hope they are. Could they decently do less?" said she.

"And fancy the mental struggles that must be going on in their brains," he urged. "If I were a man in such a situation I'd throw myself upon the woman's mercy. I'd say, 'Beautiful, sweet lady! I know I know you. Your name, your entirely charming and appropriate name, is trembling on the tip of my tongue. But, for some unaccountable reason, my brute of a memory chooses to play the fool. If you've a spark of Christian kindness in your soul, you'll come to my rescue with a little clue."

"If the woman had a Christian sense of the ridiculous in her soul, I fear you'd throw yourself on her mercy in vain," she warned.

"What *is* the good of tantalizing people?"

"Besides," she continued, "the woman might reasonably feel slightly humiliated to find herself forgotten in that bare-faced manner."

"The humiliation would be surely all the man's. Have you heard from the Wohenhoffens lately?"

"The—what? The—who?" She raised her eyebrows.

"The Wohenhoffens," he repeated.

"What are the Wohenhoffens? Are they persons? Are they things?"

1858

"Oh, nothing. My inquiry was merely dictated by a thirst for knowledge. It occurred to me that you might have won a black domino at the masked ball they gave, the Wohenhoffens. Are you sure you didn't?"

"I've a great mind to punish your forgetfulness by pretending that I did," she teased.

"She was rather tall, like you, and she had gray eyes, and a nice voice, and a laugh that was sweeter than the singing of nightingales. She was monstrously clever, too, with a flow of language that would have made her a leader in any sphere. She was also a perfect fiend. I have always been anxious to meet her again, in order that I might ask her to marry me. I'm strongly disposed to believe that she was you. Was she?" he pleaded.

"If I say yes, will you at once proceed to ask me to marry you?" she asked.

"Try it and see."

"*Ce n'est pas la peine*. It occasionally happens that a woman's already got a husband."

"She said she was an old maid."

"Do you dare to insinuate that I look like an old maid?" she cried.

"Yes."

"Upon my word!"

"Would you wish me to insinute that you look like anything so insipid as a young girl? *Were* you the woman of the black domino?" he persisted.

"I should need further information, before being able to make up my mind. Are the—what's their name?—Wohenheimer?—are the Wohenheimers people one can safely confess to knowing? Oh, you're a man, and don't count. But a woman? It sounds a trifle Jewish, Wohenheimer. But of course there are Jews and Jews."

"You're playing with me like the cat in the adage," he

sighed. "It's too cruel. No one is responsible for his memory."

"And to think that this man took me down to dinner not two months ago!" she murmured in her veil.

"You're as hard as nails. In whose house? Or—stay. Prompt me a little. Tell me the first syllable of your name. Then the rest will come with a rush."

"My name is Matilda Muggins."

"I've a great mind to punish your untruthfulness by pretending to believe you," said he. "Have you really got a husband?"

"Why do you doubt it?" said she.

"I don't doubt it. Have you?"

"I don't know what to answer."

"Don't you know whether you've got a husband?" he protested.

"I don't know what I'd better let you believe. Yes, on the whole, I think you may as well assume that I've got a husband," she concluded.

"And a lover, too?" he asked.

"Really! I like your impertinence!" she bridled.

"I only asked to show a polite interest. I knew the answer would be an indignant negative. You're an Englishwoman, and you're *nice*. Oh, one can see with half an eye that you're *nice*. But that a nice Englishwoman should have a lover is as inconceivable as that she should have side-whiskers. It's only the reg'lar bad-uns in England who have lovers. There's nothing between the family pew and the divorce court. One nice Englishwoman is a match for the whole Eleven Thousand Virgins of Cologne."

"To hear you talk, one might fancy you were not English yourself. For a man of the name of Field, you're uncommonly foreign. You *look* rather foreign, too, you know, by-the-bye. You haven't at all an English cast of countenance," she considered.

"I've enjoyed the advantages of a foreign education. I was brought up abroad," he explained.

"Where your features unconsciously assimilated themselves to a foreign type? Where you learned a hundred thousand strange little foreign things, no doubt? And imbibed a hundred thousand unprincipled little foreign notions? And all the ingenuous little foreign prejudices and misconceptions concerning England?" she questioned.

"Most of them," he assented.

"*Perfide Albion?* English hypocrisy?" she pursued.

"Oh, yes, the English are consummate hypocrites. But there's only one objection to their hypocrisy—it so rarely covers any wickedness. It's such a disappointment to see a creature stalking toward you, laboriously draped in sheep's clothing, and then to discover that it's only a sheep. You, for instance, as I took the liberty of intimating a moment ago, in spite of your perfectly respectable appearance, are a perfectly respectable woman. If you weren't, wouldn't I be making furious love to you, though!"

"As I am, I can see no reason why you shouldn't make furious love to me, if it would amuse you. There's no harm in firing your pistol at a person who's bullet-proof," she laughed.

"No; it's merely a wanton waste of powder and shot," said he. "However, I shouldn't stick at that. The deuce of it is— You permit the expression?"

"I'm devoted to the expression."

"The deuce of it is, you profess to be married."

"Do you mean to say that you, with your unprincipled foreign notions, would be restrained by any such consideration as that?" she wondered.

"I shouldn't be for an instant—if I weren't in love with you."

"*Comment donc? Déjà?*" she cried with a laugh.

"Oh, *déjà!* Why not? Consider the weather—consider the scene. Is the air soft, is it fragrant? Look at the sky—good heavens!—and the clouds, and the shadows on the grass, and the sunshine between the trees. The world is made of light to-day, of light and color, and perfume and music. *Tutt 'intorno canta amor, amor, amor!* What would you have? One recognises one's affinity. One doesn't need a lifetime. You began the business at the Wohenhoffens' ball. To-day you've merely put on the finishing touches."

"Oh, then I *am* the woman you met at the masked ball?" she cried.

"Look me in the eye, and tell me you're not," he defied her.

"I haven't the faintest interest in telling you I'm not. On the contrary, it rather pleases me to let you imagine that I am."

"She owed me a grudge, you know. I hoodwinked her like everything," he confided.

"Oh, did you? Then, as a sister woman, I should be glad to serve as her instrument of vengeance. Do you happen to have such a thing as a watch about you?" she inquired.

"Yes," he said.

"Will you be good enough to tell me what o'clock it is?"

"What are your motives for asking?"

"I'm expected at home at five."

"Where do you live?"

"What are the motives for asking?"

"I want to call upon you."

"You might wait till you're invited."

"Well, invite me—quick!"

"Never."

"Never?"

"Never, never, never," she asseverated. "A man who's forgotten me as you have!"

"But if I've only met you once at a masked ball—"

"Can't you be brought to realise that every time you mistake me for that woman of the masked ball you turn the dagger in the wound?" she demanded.

"But if you won't invite me to call upon you, how and when am I to see you again?"

"I haven't an idea," she answered, cheerfully. "I must go now. Good-by." She rose.

"One moment," he interposed. "Before you go will you allow me to look at the palm of your left hand?"

"What for?"

"I can tell fortunes. I'm extremely good at it," he boasted. "I'll tell you yours."

"Oh, very well," she assented, sitting down again: and guilelessly she pulled off her glove.

He took her hand, a beautifully slender, nervous hand, warm and soft, with rosy, tapering fingers.

"Oho! you *are* an old maid after all," he cried. "There's no wedding ring."

"You villain!" she gasped, snatching the hand away.

"I promised to tell your fortune. Haven't I told it correctly?"

"You needn't rub it in, though. Eccentric old maids don't like to be reminded of their condition."

"Will you marry *me?*"

"Why do you ask?"

"Partly for curiosity. Partly because it's the only way

1863

I can think of, to make sure of seeing you again. And then, I like your hair. Will you?"

"I can't," she said.

"Why not?"

"The stars forbid. And I'm ambitious. In my horoscope it is written that I shall either never marry at all, or—marry royalty."

"Oh, bother ambition! Cheat your horoscope. Marry me. Will you?"

"If you care to follow me," she said, rising again, "you can come and help me to commit a little theft."

He followed her to an obscure and sheltered corner of a flowery path, where she stopped before a bush of white lilac.

"There are no keepers in sight, are there?" she questioned.

"I don't see any," he said.

"Then allow me to make you a receiver of stolen goods," said she, breaking off a spray, and handing it to him.

"Thank you. But I'd rather have an answer to my question."

"Isn't that an answer?"

"Is it?"

"White lilac—to the Invisible Prince?"

"The Invisible Prince— Then you *are the black* domino!" he exclaimed.

"Oh, I suppose so," she consented.

"And you *will* marry me?"

"I'll tell the aunt I live with to ask you to dinner."

"But will you marry me?"

"I thought you wished me to cheat my horoscope?"

"How could you find a better means of doing so?"

"What! if I should marry Louis Leczinski—?"

"Oh, to be sure. You will have it that I was Louis Leczinski. But, on that subject, I must warn you seriously—"

"One instant," she interrupted. "People must look other people straight in the face when they're giving serious warnings. Look straight into my eyes, and continue your serious warning."

"I must really warn you seriously," said he, biting his lip, "that if you persist in that preposterous delusion about my being Louis Leczinski, you'll be most awfully sold. I have nothing on earth to do with Louis Leczinski. Your ingenious little theories, as I tried to convince you at the time, were absolute romance."

Her eyebrows raised a little, she kept her eyes fixed steadily on his—oh, in the drollest fashion, with a gaze that seemed to say "How admirably you do it! I wonder whether you imagine I believe you. Oh, you fibber! Aren't you ashamed to tell me such abominable fibs—?"

They stood still, eyeing each other thus, for something like twenty seconds, and then they both laughed and walked on.

WHY WAIT FOR DEATH AND TIME?

BY BERT LESTON TAYLOR

I hold it truth with him who weekly sings
    Brave songs of hope,—the music of "The Sphere,"—
That deathless tomes the living present brings:
    Great literature is with us year on year.
Books of the mighty dead, whom men revere,
    Remind me I can make *my* books sublime.
But, prithee, bay my brow while I am here:
    Why do we ever wait for Death and Time?

Shakespeare, great spirit, beat his mighty wings,
    As I beat mine, for the occasion near.
He knew, as I, the worth of present things:
    Great literature is with us year on year.
Methinks I meet across the gulf his clear
    And tranquil eye; his calm reflections chime
With mine: "Why do we at the present fleer?
    Why do we ever wait for Death and Time?"

The reading world with acclamation rings
    For my last book. It led the list at Weir,
Altoona, Rahway, Painted Post, Hot Springs:
    Great literature is with us year on year.
"The Bookman" gives me a vociferous cheer.
    Howells approves. I can no higher climb.
Bring, then, the laurel: crown my bright career—
    Why do we ever wait for Death and Time?

1866

BERT LESTON TAYLOR

Critics, who pastward, ever pastward peer,
Great literature is with us year on year.
Trumpet my fame while I am in my prime:
Why do we ever wait for Death and Time?

1867

WINTER JOYS

BY EUGENE FIELD

A man stood on the bathroom floor,
　　While raged the storm without,
One hand was on the water valve,
　　The other on the spout.

He fiercely tried to turn the plug,
　　But all in vain he tried,
"I see it all, I am betrayed,
　　The water's froze," he cried.

Down to the kitchen then he rushed,
　　And in the basement dove,
Long strived he for to turn the plugs,
　　But all in vain he strove.

"The hydrant may be running yet,"
　　He cried in hopeful tone,
Alas, the hydrant too, was froze,
　　As stiff as any stone.

There came a burst, the water pipes
　　And plugs, oh, where were they?
Ask of the soulless plumber man
　　Who called around next day.

1868

THE DEMON OF THE STUDY

BY JOHN GREENLEAF WHITTIER

The Brownie sits in the Scotchman's room,
    And eats his meat and drinks his ale,
And beats the maid with her unused broom,
    And the lazy lout with his idle flail;
But he sweeps the floor and threshes the corn,
And hies him away ere the break of dawn.

The shade of Denmark fled from the sun,
    And the Cocklane ghost from the barn-loft cheer,
The fiend of Faust was a faithful one,
    Agrippa's demon wrought in fear,
And the devil of Martin Luther sat
By the stout monk's side in social chat.

The Old Man of the Sea, on the neck of him
    Who seven times crossed the deep,
Twined closely each lean and withered limb,
    Like the nightmare in one's sleep.
But he drank of the wine, and Sindbad cast
The evil weight from his back at last.

But the demon that cometh day by day
    To my quiet room and fireside nook,
Where the casement light falls dim and gray
    On faded painting and ancient book,
Is a sorrier one than any whose names
Are chronicled well by good King James.

1869

THE DEMON OF THE STUDY

No bearer of burdens like Caliban,
   No runner of errands like Ariel,
He comes in the shape of a fat old man,
   Without rap of knuckle or pull of bell;
And whence he comes, or whither he goes,
I know as I do of the wind which blows.

A stout old man with a greasy hat
   Slouched heavily down to his dark, red nose,
And two gray eyes enveloped in fat,
   Looking through glasses with iron bows.
Read ye, and heed ye, and ye who can,
Guard well your doors from that old man!

He comes with a careless "How d'ye do?"
   And seats himself in my elbow-chair;
And my morning paper and pamphlet new
   Fall forthwith under his special care,
And he wipes his glasses and clears his throat,
And, button by button, unfolds his coat.

And then he reads from paper and book,
   In a low and husky asthmatic tone,
With the stolid sameness of posture and look
   Of one who reads to himself alone;
And hour after hour on my senses come
That husky wheeze and that dolorous hum.

The price of stocks, the auction sales,
   The poet's song and the lover's glee,
The horrible murders, the sea-board gales,
   The marriage list, and the *jeu d'esprit,*
All reach my ear in the self-same tone,—
I shudder at each, but the fiend reads on!

1870

Oh, sweet as the lapse of water at noon
　O'er the mossy roots of some forest tree,
The sigh of the wind in the woods of June,
　Or sound of flutes o'er a moonlight sea,
Or the low soft music, perchance, which seems
To float through the slumbering singer's dreams,

So sweet, so dear is the silvery tone,
　Of her in whose features I sometimes look,
As I sit at eve by her side alone,
　And we read by turns, from the self-same book,
Some tale perhaps of the olden time,
Some lover's romance or quaint old rhyme.

Then when the story is one of woe,—
　Some prisoner's plaint through his dungeon-bar,
Her blue eye glistens with tears, and low,
　Her voice sinks down like a moan afar;
And I seem to hear that prisoner's wail,
And his face looks on me worn and pale.

And when she reads some merrier song,
　Her voice is glad as an April bird's,
And when the tale is of war and wrong,
　A trumpet's summons is in her words,
And the rush of the hosts I seem to hear,
And see the tossing of plume and spear!

Oh, pity me then, when, day by day,
　The stout fiend darkens my parlor door;
And reads me perchance the self-same lay
　Which melted in music, the night before,
From lips as the lips of Hylas sweet,
And moved like twin roses which zephyrs meet!

1871

THE DEMON OF THE STUDY

I cross my floor with a nervous tread,
  I whistle and laugh and sing and shout,
I flourish my cane above his head,
  And stir up the fire to roast him out;
I topple the chairs, and drum on the pane,
And press my hands on my ears, in vain!

I've studied Glanville and James the wise.
  And wizard black-letter tomes which treat
Of demons of every name and size
  Which a Christian man is presumed to meet,
But never a hint and never a line
Can I find of a reading fiend like mine.

I've crossed the Psalter with Brady and Tate,
  And laid the Primer above them all,
I've nailed a horseshoe over the grate,
  And hung a wig to my parlor wall
Once worn by a learned Judge, they say,
At Salem court in the witchcraft day!

"Conjuro te, sceleratissime,
  Abire ad tuum locum!"—still
Like a visible nightmare he sits by me,—
  The exorcism has lost its skill;
And I hear again in my haunted room
The husky wheeze and the dolorous hum!

Ah! commend me to Mary Magdalen
  With her sevenfold plagues, to the wandering Jew,
To the terrors which haunted Orestes when
  The furies his midnight curtains drew,
But charm him off, ye who charm him can,
That reading demon, that fat old man!

1872

UNCLE BENTLEY AND THE ROOSTERS

BY HAYDEN CARRUTH

The burden of Uncle Bentley has always rested heavily on our town. Having not a shadow of business to attend to he has made other people's business his own, and looked after it in season and out—especially out. If there is a thing which nobody wants done, to this Uncle Bentley applies his busy hand.

One warm summer Sunday we were all at church. Our pastor had taken the passage on turning the other cheek, or one akin to it, for his text, and was preaching on peace and quiet and non-resistance. He soon had us in a devout mood which must have been beautiful to see and encouraging to the good man.

Of course, Uncle Bentley was there—he always was, and forever in a front pew, with his neck craned up looking backward to see if there was anything that didn't need doing which he could do. He always tinkered with the fires in the winter and fussed with the windows in the summer, and did his worst with each. His strongest church point was ushering. Not content to usher the stranger within our gates, he would usher all of us, and always thrust us into pews with just the people we didn't want to sit with. If you failed to follow him when he took you in tow, he would stop and look back reproachfully, describing mighty indrawing curves with his arm; and if you pretended not to see him, he would give a low

1873

whistle to attract your attention, the arm working right along, like a Holland windmill.

On this particular warm summer Sunday Uncle Bentley was in place wearing his long, full-skirted coat, a queer, dark, bottle-green, purplish blue. He had ushered to his own exceeding joy, and got two men in one pew, and given them a single hymn-book, who wouldn't on week-days speak to each other. I ought to mention that we had long before made a verb of Uncle Bentley. To unclebentley was to do the wrong thing. It was a regular verb, unclebentley, unclebentleyed, unclebentleying. Those two rampant enemies in the same pew had been unclebentleyed.

The minister was floating along smoothly on the subject of peace when Uncle Bentley was observed to throw up his head. He had heard a sound outside. It was really nothing but one of Deacon Plummer's young roosters crowing. The Deacon lived near, and vocal offerings from his poultry were frequent and had ceased to interest any one except Uncle Bentley. Then in the pauses between the preacher's periods we heard the flapping of wings, with sudden stoppings and startings. Those unregenerate fowls, unable to understand the good man's words, were fighting. Even this didn't interest us—we were committed to peace. But Uncle Bentley shot up like a jack-in-a-box and cantered down the aisle. Of course, his notion was that the roosters were disturbing the services, and that it was his duty to go out and stop them. We heard vigorous "Shoos!" and "Take thats!" and "Consairn yous!" and then Uncle Bentley came back looking very important, and as he stalked up the aisle he glanced around and nodded his head, saying as clearly as words, "There, where would you be without me?" Another defiant crow floated in at the window.

The next moment the rushing and beating of wings began again, and down the aisle went Uncle Bentley, the long tails of that coat fairly floating like a cloud behind him. There was further uproar outside, and Uncle Bentley was back in his place, this time turning around and whispering hoarsely, "I fixed 'em!" But such was not the case, for twice more the very same thing was repeated. The last time Uncle Bentley came back he wore a calm, snug expression, as who should say, "Now I *have* fixed 'em!" We should have liked it better if the roosters had fixed Uncle Bentley. But nobody paid much attention except Deacon Plummer. The thought occurred to him that perhaps Uncle Bentley had killed the fowls. But he hadn't.

However, there was no more disturbance without, and after a time the sermon closed. There was some sort of a special collection to be taken up. Of course, Uncle Bentley always insisted on taking up all the collections. He hopped up on this occasion and seized the plate with more than usual vigor. His struggles with the roosters had evidently stimulated him. He soon made the rounds and approached the table in front of the pulpit to deposit his harvest. As he did so we saw to our horror that the long tails of that ridiculous coat were violently agitated. A sickening suspicion came over us. The next moment one of those belligerent young roosters thrust a head out of either of those coat-tail pockets. One uttered a raucous crow, the other made a vicious dab. Uncle Bentley dropped the plate with a scattering of coin, seized a coat skirt in each hand, and drew it front. This dumped both fowls out on the floor, where they went at it hammer and tongs. What happened after this is a blur in most of our memories. All that is certain is that there was an uproar in the congregation, especially the younger portion; that the Deacon began making unsuccessful dives for his poultry; that the organist struck up "Onward, Christian Soldiers," and that the minister waved us away without a benediction amid loud shouts of, "Shoo!" "I swanny!" and, "Drat the pesky critters!" from your Uncle Bentley.

Did it serve to subdue Uncle Bentley? Not in the least; he survived to do worse things.

1876

A SHINING MARK

BY IRONQUILL

A man came here from Idaho,
  With lots of mining stock.
He brought along as specimens
  A lot of mining rock.

The stock was worth a cent a pound
  If stacked up in a pile.
The rock was worth a dollar and
  'A half per cubic mile.

We planted him at eventide,
  'Mid shadows dim and dark;
We fixed him up an epitaph,—
  "Death loves a mining shark."

1877

A BOOKWORM'S PLAINT*

BY CLINTON SCOLLARD

To-day, when I had dined my fill
Upon a Caxton,—you know Will,—
I crawled forth o'er the colophon
To bask awhile within the sun;
And having coiled my sated length,
I felt anon my whilom strength
Slip from me gradually, till deep
I dropped away in dreamful sleep,
Wherein I walked an endless maze,
And dined on Caxtons all my days.

Then I woke suddenly. Alas!
What in my sleep had come to pass?
That priceless first edition row,—
Squat quarto and tall folio,—
Had, in my slumber, vanished quite;
Instead, on my astonished sight
The newest novels burst,—a gay
And most unpalatable array!
I, that have battened on the best,
Why should I thus be dispossessed
And with starvation, or the worst
Of diets, cruelly be curst?

* Lippincott's Magazine.

1878

A POE-'EM OF PASSION

BY CHARLES F. LUMMIS

It was many and many a year ago,
  On an island near the sea,
That a maiden lived whom you mightn't know
  By the name of Cannibalee;
And this maiden she lived with no other thought
  Than a passionate fondness for me.

I was a child, and she was a child—
  Tho' her tastes were adult Feejee—
But she loved with a love that was more than love,
  My yearning Cannibalee;
With a love that could take me roast or fried
  Or raw, as the case might be.

And that is the reason that long ago,
  In that island near the sea,
I had to turn the tables and eat
  My ardent Cannibalee—
Not really because I was fond of her,
  But to check her fondness for me.

But the stars never rise but I think of the size
  Of my hot-potted Cannibalee,
And the moon never stares but it brings me night-
      mares
  Of my spare-rib Cannibalee;

1879

And all the night-tide she is restless inside,
Is my still indigestible dinner-belle bride,
In her pallid tomb, which is Me,
In her solemn sepulcher, Me.

THE REAL DIARY OF A REAL BOY

BY HENRY A. SHUTE

Mar. 11, 186—Went to church in the morning. the fernace was all write. Mister Lennard preeched about loving our ennymies, and told every one if he had any angry feelings towards ennyone to go to him and shake hands and see how much better you wood feel. i know how it is becaus when me and Beany are mad we dont have eny fun and when we make up the one who is to blam always wants to treet. why when Beany was mad with me becaus i went home from Gil Steels surprise party with Lizzie Towle, Ed Towles sister, he woodent speak to me for 2 days, and when we made up he treated me to ice cream with 2 spoons and he let me dip twice to his once. he took pretty big dips to make up. Beany is mad if enny of the fellers go with Lizzie Towle. she likes Beany better than she does enny of the fellers and Beany ought to be satisfied, but sometimes he acks mad when i go down there to fite roosters with Ed. i gess he needent worry much, no feller isnt going to leave of fiting roosters to go with no girls. well i most forgot that i was going to say, but after church i went up to Micky Gould who was going to fite me behind the school house, and said Micky lets be friends and Micky said, huh old Skinny, i can lick you in 2 minits and i said you aint man enuf and he called me a nockneed puke, and i called him a wall eyed lummix and he give me a paist in the eye and i gave him a good one in the mouth, and then we rassled and Micky threw

1881

me and i turned him, and he got hold of my new false bosom and i got hold of his hair, and the fellers all hollered hit him Micky, paist him Skinny, and Mister Purington, Pewts father pulled us apart and i had Mickys paper collar and necktie and some of his hair and he had my false bosom and when i got home father made me go to bed and stay there all the afternoon for fiting, but i guess he didnt like my losing my false bosom. ennyway he asked me how many times i hit Micky and which licked. he let me get up at supper time. next time i try to love my ennymy i am a going to lick him first.

Went to a sunday school concert in the evening. Keene and Cele sung now i lay me down to sleep. they was a lot of people sung together and Mister Gale beat time. Charlie Gerish played the violin and Miss Packard sung. i was scart when Keene and Cele sung for i was afraid they would break down, but they dident, and people said they sung like night harks. i gess if they knowed how night harks sung they woodent say much. father felt pretty big and to hear him talk you wood think he did the singing. he give them ten cents apeace. i dident get none. you gest wait, old man till i git my cornet.

Went to a corcus last night. me and Beany were in the hall in the afternoon helping Bob Carter sprinkle the floor and put on the sordust. the floor was all shiny with wax and aufully slipery. so Bob got us to put on some water to take off the shiny wax. well write in front of the platform there is a low platform where they get up to put in their votes and then step down and Beany said, dont put any water there only jest dry sordust. so i dident. well that night we went erly to see the fun. Gim Luverin got up and said there was one man which was the oldest voter in town and he ought to vote the first, the name of this destinkuished sitizen was John Quincy Ann Pollard. then

old mister Pollard got up and put in his vote and when
he stepped down his heels flew up and he went down whak
on the back of his head and 2 men lifted him up and
lugged him to a seat, and then Ed Derborn, him that rings
the town bell, stepped up pretty lively and went flat and
swort terrible, and me and Beany nearly died we laffed
so. well it kept on, people dident know what made them
fall, and Gim Odlin sat write down in his new umbrella
and then they sent me down stairs for a pail of wet sordust and when i was coming up i heard an awful whang,
and when i got up in the hall they were lugging old mister
Stickney off to die and they put water on his head and
lugged him home in a hack. me and Beany dont know
what to do. if we dont tell, Bob will lose his place and if
we do we will get licked.

Mar. 31. April fool day tomorrow. i am laying for
Beany. old Francis licked 5 fellers today becaus they
sung rong when we was singing speek kindly it is better
for to rule by luv than feer.

June 14. Rashe Belnap and Horris Cobbs go in swimming every morning at six o'clock. i got a licking today
that beat the one Beany got. last summer me and Tomtit
Tomson and Cawcaw Harding and Whack and Poz and
Boog Chadwick went in swimming in May and all thru
the summer until October. one day i went in 10 times.
well i dident say anything about it to father so as not to
scare him. well today he dident go to Boston and he said
i am going to teech you to swim. when i was as old as
you i cood swim said he, and you must lern, i said i have
been wanting to lern to swim, for all the other boys can
swim. so we went down to the gravil and i peeled off
my close and got ready, now said he, you jest wade in up
to your waste and squat down and duck your head under.
i said the water will get in my nose. he said no it wont

jest squat rite down. i cood see him laffin when he thought i wood snort and sputter.

so i waded out a little ways and then div in and swam under water most across, and when i came up i looked to see if father was surprised. gosh you aught to have seen him. he had pulled off his coat and vest and there he stood up to his waste in the water with his eyes jest bugging rite out as big as hens eggs, and he was jest a going to dive for my dead body. then i turned over on my back and waved my hand at him. he dident say anything for a minute, only he drawed in a long breth. then he began to look foolish, and then mad, and then he turned and started to slosh back to the bank where he slipped and went in all over. When he got to the bank he was pretty mad and yelled for me to come out. when i came out he cut a stick and whaled me, and as soon as i got home he sent me to bed for lying, but i gess he was mad becaus i about scart the life out of him. but that nite i heard him telling mother about it and he said that he div 3 times for me in about thirty feet of water. but he braged about my swimming and said i cood swim like a striped frog. i shall never forget how his boots went kerslosh kerslosh kerslosh when we were skinning home thru croslots. i shall never forget how that old stick hurt either. ennyhow he dident say ennything about not going in again, so i gess i am all rite.

June 15, 186—Johnny Heeld, a student, came to me and wanted me to carry some tickets to a dance round to the girls in the town. there was about 1 hundred of them. he read the names over to me and i said i knew them all. so after school me and Beany started out and walked all over town and give out the tickets. i had a long string of names and every time i wood leave one i wood mark out the name. i dident give the Head girls any because they told father about some things that me and Beany and Pewt did and the Parmer girls and the Cilley girls lived way up on the plains and i dident want to walk up there, so when i went over to Hemlock side to give one, i went over to the factory boarding house and give some to them. they was auful glad to get them too and said they would go to the dance. some people was not at home and so i gave their tickets to the next house. it took me till 8 o'clock and i got 1 dollar for it. i dont believe those girls that dident get their tickets will care much about going ennyway. i gess the Head girls wont want to tell on me another time.

June 23. there is a dead rat in the wall in my room. it smells auful.

A MOTHERS' MEETING*

BY MADELINE BRIDGES

"Where's the maternal parent of
   This boy that stands in need of beating,
And of this babe that pines for love?"
   "Oh, she is at a Mothers' Meeting!"

"Fair daughter, why these young tears shed,
   For passion's tale, too sweet and fleeting,
Lonely and mute, uncomforted?"
   "My mother's at a Mothers' Meeting."

"Man, whom misfortunes jeer and taunt,
   Whom frauds forsake, and hope is cheating,
Fly to your mother's arms." "I can't—
   You see, she's at a Mothers' Meeting."

Alas, what next will woman do?
   Love, duty, children, home, maltreating,
The while she, smiling, rallies to
   The roll-call of a Mothers' Meeting!

*Lippincott's Magazine.

1886

MISTER RABBIT'S LOVE AFFAIR

BY FRANK L. STANTON

One day w'en Mister Rabbit wuz a-settin' in de grass
He see Miss Mary comin', en he wouldn't let her pass,
Kaze he know she lookin' purty in de river lookin'glass,
    O Mister Rabbit, in de mawnin'!

But de Mockin'bird wuz singin' in de blossom en de dew,
En he know 'bout Mister Rabbit, en he watchin' er 'im,
    too;
En Miss Mary heah his music, en she tell 'im "Howdy-
    do!"
    O Mister Rabbit, in de mawnin'!

Mister Rabbit 'low he beat 'im, en he say he'll l'arn ter
    sing,
En he tried it all de winter, en he kep' it up in spring;
But he wuzn't buil' fer singin', kaze he lack de voice en
    wing,—
    Good-by, Mister Rabbit, in de mawnin'!

1887

OUR HIRED GIRL

BY JAMES WHITCOMB RILEY

Our hired girl, she's 'Lizabuth Ann;
　　An' she can cook best things to eat!
She ist puts dough in our pie-pan,
　　An' pours in somepin' 'at's good and sweet,
An' nen she salts it all on top
With cinnamon; an' nen she'll stop
　　An' stoop an' slide it, ist as slow,
In th' old cook-stove, so's 'twon't slop
　　An' git all spilled; nen bakes it, so
It's custard pie, first thing you know!
　　　An' nen she'll say:
　"Clear out o' my way!
　　They's time fer work, an' time fer play!—
　　　Take yer dough, an' run, Child; run!
　　　Er I cain't git no cookin' done!"

When our hired girl 'tends like she's mad,
　　An' says folks got to walk the chalk
When *she's* around, er wisht they had,
　　I play out on our porch an' talk
To th' Raggedy Man 'at mows our lawn;
An' he says *"Whew!"* an' nen leans on
　　His old crook-scythe, and blinks his eyes
An' sniffs all round an' says,—"I swawn!
　　Ef my old nose don't tell me lies,
1888

It 'pears like I smell custard-pies!"
  An' nen *he'll* say,—
" 'Clear out o' my way!
  They's time fer work an' time fer play!
    Take yer dough, an' run, Child; run!
    Er *she* cain't git no cookin done!' "

Wunst our hired girl, one time when she
  Got the supper, an' we all et,
An' it was night, an' Ma an' me
  An' Pa went wher' the "Social" met,—
An' nen when we come home, an' see
A light in the kitchen-door, an' we
  Heerd a maccordeum, Pa says "Lan'-
O'-Gracious! who can *her* beau be?"
  An' I marched in, an' 'Lizabuth Ann
  Wuz parchin' corn fer the Raggedy Man!
    Better say
  "Clear out o' the way!
  They's time fer work, an' time fer play!
    Take the hint, an' run, Child; run!
    Er we cain't git no *courtin'* done!"

THE REASON

BY IRONQUILL

Says John last night:
   "William, by grab! I'm beat
To know why stolen kisses
   Taste so sweet."

Says William: "Sho!
   That's easily explained—
It's 'cause they're *syrup*-
   titiously obtained."

. . . .

O cruel thought!
   O words of cruel might!
The coroner
   He sat on John that night.

1890

ONCL' ANTOINE ON 'CHANGE

BY WALLACE BRUCE AMSBARY

(Antoine Boisvert, Raconteur.)

I've jus' com' from Chicago town,
　A seein' all de sights
From stockyard to de ballet gairl,
　All drass' in spangled tights.
But all de worstes' nonsens'
　T'roo vich I got to wade,
I t'ink de t'ing dat gats de cake
　Ees place called Board of Trade.

I heard moch talk about dem chap
　Dey call de Bull an' Bear,
Dat play aroun' with price of stock
　An' get you unaware.
Who'll tell you w'at your wheat
　Will bring in Fevuary nex',
In jus' so smood an' quiet vay
　De curé read his tex'.

An' dere dey vere out on de floor,
　De mans who mak' de price
Of all de country produce,
　A lookin' smood an' nice.
But dey had vink opon dere eye
　Dat look you t'roo an' t'roo,
Like tricky bunko steerer ven
　He's hunting after you.

1891

Dey got de ball to roll ver' swif'
  An' firs' fall from de dock
Vas bottom off on July pork;
  An' heem dat held de stock
Commence to hiss an' wriggle
  Lak' a yellow rattlesnake;
De res' buzz jus' lak' bumblebee
  Stirred op vit hayin' rake.

Dis bottom off on July pork
  Is strike me kin' of queer,
I's t'ink dat hogs is good for eat
  Mos' all of de 'hole year.
Dose feller on Chicago town
  Is mak' such fonny phrase
Dat—*entre nous*—I sometimes t'ink
  Dat som' of dem ees craz'.

Den dere ees somet'ing happen
  Dat mak' 'em more excite',
W'en news ees com' overe de vires
  Dat Boer an' Britain fight,
I nevere saw such meex-op yet,
  In days since I be born,
Dey scowl an' call wan nodder names,
  Dere faces show moch scorn.

Wan man grow wild an' mos'ly craz',
  De tears stream off his eyes,
Dere's nodder man dat's laf an' shout,
  It's mak' me mos' surprise.
I guess it mak' som' differ*ance*
  Vich side you're on de fence,
But in dis Bear an' Bull meex-op
  I see not ver' moch sense.

1892

HEZEKIAH BEDOTT'S OPINION

BY FRANCES M. WHICHER

He was a wonderful hand to moralize, husband was, 'specially after he begun to enjoy poor health. He made an observation once when he was in one of his poor turns, that I never shall forget the longest day I live. He says to me one winter evenin' as we was a settin' by the fire,— I was a knittin' (I was always a wonderful great knitter) and he was a smokin' (he was a master hand to smoke, though the doctor used to tell him he'd be better off to let tobacker alone; when he was well he used to take his pipe and smoke a spell after he'd got the chores done up, and when he wa'n't well, used to smoke the biggest part of the time). Well, he took his pipe out of his mouth and turned toward me, and I knowed something was comin', for he had a pertikkeler way of lookin' round when he was gwine to say anything oncommon. Well, he says to me, says he, "Silly" (my name was Prissilly naterally, but he ginerally called me "Silly," cause 'twas handier, you know). Well, he says to me, says he, "Silly," and he looked pretty sollem, I tell you—he had a sollem coun-tenance naterally—and after he got to be deacon 'twas more so, but since he'd lost his health he looked sollemer than ever, and certainly you wouldent wonder at it if you knowed how much he underwent. He was troubled with a wonderful pain in his chest, and amazin' weakness in the spine of his back, besides the pleurissy in the side, and having the ager a considerable part of the time, and bein' broke of his rest o' nights 'cause he was so put to 't for breath when he laid down. Why it's an onaccountable fact that when that man died he hadent seen a well day in fifteen year, though when he was married and for five or six years after I shouldent desire to see a ruggeder man that he was. But the time I'm speakin' of he'd been out o' health nigh upon ten year, and O dear sakes! how he had altered since the first time I ever see him! That was to a quiltin' to Squire Smith's a spell afore Sally was married. I'd no idee then that Sal Smith was a gwine to be married to Sam Pendergrass. She'd ben keepin' company with Mose Hewlitt, for better'n a year, and everybody said *that* was a settled thing, and lo and behold! all of a sudding she up and took Sam Pendergrass. Well, that was the first time I ever see my husband, and if anybody'd a told me then that I should ever marry him, I should a said—but lawful sakes! I most forgot, I was gwine to tell you what he said to me that evenin', and when a body begins to tell a thing I believe in finishin' on't some time or other. Some folks have a way of talkin' round and round and round forevermore, and never come to the pint. Now there's Miss Jinkins, she that was Poll Bingham afore she was married, she is the tejusest indi- vidooal to tell a story that ever I see in all my born days. But I was a gwine to tell you what husband said. He says to me, says he, "Silly"; says I, "What?" I dident say, "What, Hezekier?" for I dident like his name. The first time I ever heard it I near killed myself a laffin. "Heze- kier Bedott," says I, "well, I would give up if I had sich a name," but then you know I had no more idee o' marry- in' the feller than you had this minnit o' marryin' the gov- ernor. I s'pose you think it's curus we should a named our oldest son Hezekiah. Well, we done it to please father and mother Bedott; it's father Bedott's name, and he and mother Bedott both used to think that names had ought to go down from gineration to gineration. But we always called him Kier, you know. Speakin' o' Kier, he is a blessin', ain't he? and I ain't the only one that thinks so, I guess. Now don't you never tell nobody that I said so, but between you and me I rather guess that if Kezier Winkle thinks she is a gwine to ketch Kier Bedott she is a *leetle* out of her reckonin'. But I was going to tell what husband said. He says to me, says he, "Silly"; I says, says I, "What?" If I dident say "what" when he said "Silly" he'd a kept on saying "Silly," from time to eternity. He always did, because you know, he wanted me to pay pertikkeler attention, and I ginerally did; no woman was ever more attentive to her husband than what I was. Well, he says to me, says he, "Silly." Says I, "What?" though I'd no idee what he was gwine to say, dident know but what 'twas something about his sufferings, though he wa'n't apt to complain, but he frequently used to remark that he wouldent wish his worst enemy to suffer one minnit as he did all the time; but that can't be called grumblin'—think it can? Why I've seen him in sitivation when you'd a thought no mortal could a helped grumblin'; but *he* dident. He and me went once in the dead of winter in a one-hoss shay out to Boonville to see a sister o' hisen. You know the snow is amazin' deep in that section o' the kentry. Well, the hoss got stuck in one o' them are flambergasted snow-banks, and there we sot, onable to stir, and to cap all, while we was a sittin' there, husband was took with a dretful crik in his back. Now *that* was what I call a *perdickerment,* don't you? Most men would a swore, but husband dident. He only said, says he, "Consarn it." How did we get out, did you ask? Why we might a benn sittin' there to this day fur as *I* know, if there hadent a happened to come along a mess o' men in a double team, and they hysted us out. But I was gwine to tell you that observation of hisen. Says he to me, says he, "Silly" (I could see by the light o' the fire, there dident happen to be no candle burnin', if I don't disremember, though my memory is sometimes ruther forgitful, but I know we wa'n't apt to burn candles exceptin' when we had company)—I could see by the light of the fire that his mind was oncommon solemnized. Says he to me, says he. "Silly." I says to him, says I, "What?" He says to me, *"We're all poor critters!"*

WHAT LACK WE YET?

BY ROBERT J. BURDETTE

When Washington was president
  He was a mortal icicle;
He never on a railroad went,
  And never rode a bicycle.

He read by no electric lamp,
  Ne'er heard about the Yellowstone;
He never licked a postage stamp,
  And never saw a telephone.

His trousers ended at his knees;
  By wire he could not snatch dispatch;
He filled his lamp with whale-oil grease,
  And never had a match to scratch.

But in these days it's come to pass,
  All work is with such dashing done,
We've all these things, but then, alas—
  We seem to have no Washington!

1897

JACOB

BY PHŒBE CARY

He dwelt among "Apartments let,"
  About five stories high;
A man, I thought, that none would get,
  And very few would try.

A boulder, by a larger stone
  Half hidden in the mud,
Fair as a man when only one
  Is in the neighborhood.

He lived unknown, and few could tell
  When Jacob was not free;
But he has got a wife—and O!
  The difference to me!

1898

TO BARY JADE

BY CHARLES FOLLEN ADAMS

The bood is beabig brighdly, love;
   The sdars are shidig too;
While I ab gazig dreabily,
   Add thigkig, love, of you.
You caddot, oh! you caddot kdow,
   By darlig, how I biss you—
(Oh, whadt a fearful cold I've got!—
   Ck-*tish*-u! Ck-ck-*tish*-u!)

I'b sittig id the arbor, love,
   Where you sat by by side,
Whed od that calb, autubdal dight
   You said you'd be by bride.
Oh! for wud bobedt to caress
   Add tederly to kiss you;
Budt do! we're beddy biles apart—
   (Ho-*rash*-o! Ck-ck-*tish*-u!)

This charbig evedig brigs to bide
   The tibe whed first we bet:
It seebs budt odly yesterday;
   I thigk I see you yet.
Oh! tell be, ab I sdill your owd?
   By hopes—oh, do dot dash theb!
(Codfoud by cold, 'tis gettig worse—
   Ck-tish-u! Ch-ck-*thrash*-eb!)

1899

TO BARY JADE

Good-by, by darlig Bary Jade!
  The bid-dight hour is dear;
Add it is hardly wise, by love,
  For be to ligger here.
The heavy dews are fallig fast:
  A fod good-dight I wish you.
(Ho-*rash*-o!—there it is agaid—
  Ck-*thrash*-ub! Ck-ck-*tish*-u!)

1900

HIS GRANDMOTHER'S WAY

BY FRANK L. STANTON

Tell you, gran'mother's a queer one, shore—
  Makes your heart go pitty-pat!
If the wind just happens to open a door,
  She'll say there's "a sign" in that!
An' if no one ain't in a rockin'-chair
An' it rocks itself, she'll say: "Oh, dear!
      Oh, dear! Oh, my!
I'm afeared 'at somebody is goin' to die!"
      An' she makes me cry—
      She makes me cry!

Once wuz a owl 'at happened to light
  On our tall chimney-top,
An' screamed an' screamed in the dead o' night,
  An' nuthin' could make it stop!
An' gran'ma—she uncovered her head
An' almos' frightened me out of the bed;
      "Oh, dear; Oh, my!
I'm certain 'at some one is goin' to die!"
      An' she made me cry—
      She made me cry!

Just let a cow lean over the gate
  An' bellow, an' gran'ma—she
Will say her prayers, if it's soon or late,
  An' shake her finger at me!

An' then, an' then you'll hear her say:
"It's a sign w'en the cattle act that way!
       Oh, dear! Oh, my!
I'm certain 'at somebody's goin' to die!"
       Oh, she makes me cry—
       She makes me cry!

Skeeriest person you ever seen!
  Always a-huntin' fer "signs";
Says it's "spirits" 'at's good, or mean,
  If the wind jest shakes the vines!
I always feel skeery w'en gran'ma's aroun'—
An' think 'at I see things, an' jump at each soun':
       "Oh, dear! Oh, my!
I'm certain 'at somebody's goin' to die!"
       Oh, she makes me cry—
       She makes me cry!

1902

The Only True and Reliable Account of

THE GREAT PRIZE FIGHT,

For $100,000, at
Seal Rock Point, on Sunday Last,
Between His Excellency Gov. Stanford and Hon.
F. F. Low, Governor Elect of California.

REPORTED BY SAMUEL L. CLEMENS

For the past month the sporting world has been in a state of feverish excitement on account of the grand prize fight set for last Sunday between the two most distinguished citizens of California, for a purse of one hundred thousand dollars. The high social standing of the competitors, their exalted position in the arena of politics, together with the princely sum of money staked upon the issue of the combat, all conspired to render the proposed prize fight a subject of extraordinary importance, and to give it an éclat never before vouchsafed to such a circumstance since the world began. Additional lustre was shed upon the coming contest by the lofty character of the seconds or bottle-holders chosen by the two champions, these being no other than Judge Field (on the part of Gov. Low), Associate Justice of the Supreme Court of the United States, and Hon. Wm. M. Stewart (commonly called "Bill Stewart," or "Bullyragging Bill Stewart"), of the city of Virginia, the most popular as well as the most distinguished lawyer in Nevada Territory, member of the Constitutional Convention, and future U. S. Senator for the state of Washoe, as I hope and believe—on the part of Gov. Stanford. Principals and seconds together, it is fair to presume that such an array of talent was never entered for a combat of this description upon any previous occasion.

Stewart and Field had their men in constant training at the Mission during the six weeks preceding the contest, and such was the interest taken in the matter that thousands visited that sacred locality daily to pick up such morsels of information as they might, concerning the physical and scientific improvement being made by the gubernatorial acrobats. The anxiety manifested by the populace was intense. When it was learned that Stanford had smashed a barrel of flour to atoms with a single blow of his fist, the voice of the people was at his side. But when the news came that Low had caved in the head of a tubular boiler with one stroke of his powerful "mawley" (which term is in strict accordance with the language of the ring) the tide of opinion changed again. These changes were frequent, and they kept the minds of the public in such a state of continual vibration that I fear the habit thus acquired is confirmed, and that they will never more cease to oscillate.

The fight was to take place on last Sunday morning at ten o'clock. By nine every wheeled vehicle and every species of animal capable of bearing burthens, were in active service, and the avenues leading to the Seal Rock swarmed with them in mighty processions whose numbers no man might hope to estimate.

I determined to be upon the ground at an early hour. Now I dislike to be exploded, as it were, out of my balmy slumbers, by a sudden, stormy assault upon my door, and an imperative order to "Get up!"—wherefore I requested one of the intelligent porters of the Lick House to call at my palatial apartments, and murmur gently through the key-hole the magic monosyllable "Hash!" That "fetched me."

The urbane livery-stable keeper furnished me with a solemn, short-bodied, long-legged animal—a sort of animated counting-house stool, as it were—which he called a "Morgan" horse. He told me who the brute was "sired" by, and was proceeding to tell me who he was "dammed" by, but I gave him to understand that I was competent to damn the horse myself, and should probably do it very effectually before I got to the battle-ground. I mentioned to him, however, that I was not proposing to attend a funeral; it was hardly necessary to furnish me an animal gifted with such oppressive solemnity of bearing as distinguished his "Morgan." He said in reply, that Morgan was only pensive when in the stable, but that on the road I would find him one of the liveliest horses in the world.

He enunciated the truth.

The brute "bucked" with me from the foot of Montgomery street to the Occidental Hotel. The laughter which be provoked from the crowds of citizens along the sidewalks he took for applause, and honestly made every effort in his power to deserve it, regardless of consequences.

He was very playful, but so suddenly were the creations of his fancy conceived and executed, and so much ground did he take up with them, that it was safest to behold them from a distance. In the self-same moment of time, he shot his heels through the side of a street-car, and then backed himself into Barry and Patten's and sat down on the free-lunch table.

Such was the length of this Morgan's legs.

Between the Occidental and the Lick House, having

become thoroughly interested in his work, he planned and carried out a series of the most extraordinary ma- neuvres ever suggested by the brain of any horse. He arched his neck and went tripping daintily across the street sideways, "rairing up" on his hind legs occasion- ally, in a very disagreeable way, and looking into the sec- ond-story windows. He finally waltzed into the large ice cream saloon opposite the Lick House, and—

But the memory of that perilous voyage hath caused me to digress from the proper subject of this paper, which is the great prize fight between Governors Low and Stanford. I will resume.

After an infinitude of fearful adventures, the history of which would fill many columns of this newspaper, I finally arrived at the Seal Rock Point at a quarter to ten—two hours and a half out from San Francisco, and not less gratified than surprised that I ever got there at all—and anchored my noble Morgan to a boulder on the hillside. I had to swathe his head in blankets also, because, while my back was turned for a single moment, he developed another atrocious trait of his most remarkable character. He tried to eat little Augustus Maltravers Jackson, the "humble" but interesting offspring of Hon. J. Belvidere Jackson, a wealthy barber from San Jose. It would have been a comfort to me to leave the infant to his fate, but I did not feel able to pay for him.

When I reached the battle-ground, the great champions were already stripped and prepared for the "mill." Both were in splendid condition, and displayed a redundancy of muscle about the breast and arms which was delight- ful to the eye of the sportive connoisseur. They were well matched. Adepts said that Stanford's "heft" and tall stature were fairly offset by Low's superior litheness and activity. From their heads to the Union colors around their waists, their costumes were similar to that of the Greek slave; from thence down they were clad in flesh-colored tights and grenadier boots.

The ring was formed upon the beautiful level sandy beach above the Cliff House, and within twenty paces of the snowy surf of the broad Pacific Ocean, which was spotted here and there with monstrous sea-lions attracted shoreward by curiosity concerning the vast multitude of people collected in the vicinity.

At five minutes past ten, Brigadier-General Wright, the Referee, notified the seconds to bring their men "up to the scratch." They did so, amid the shouts of the populace, the noise whereof rose high above the roar of the sea.

First Round.—The pugilists advanced to the centre of the ring, shook hands, retired to their respective corners, and at the call of the time-keeper, came forward and went at it. Low dashed out handsomely with his left and gave Stanford a paster in the eye, and at the same moment his adversary mashed him in the ear. (These singular phrases are entirely proper, Mr. Editor—I find them in the copy of "Bell's Life in London" now lying before me.) After some beautiful sparring, both parties went down—that is to say, they went down to the bottle-holders, Stewart and Field, and took a drink.

Second Round.—Stanford launched out a well intended plunger, but Low parried it admirably and instantly busted him in the snoot. (Cries of "Bully for the Marysville Infant!") After some lively fibbing (both of them are used to it in political life,) the combatants went to grass. (See "Bell's Life.")

Third Round.—Both came up panting considerably. Low let go a terrific side-winder, but Stanford stopped it handsomely and replied with an earthquake on Low's bread-basket. (Enthusiastic shouts of "Sock it to him, my Sacramento Pet!") More fibbing—both down.

Fourth Round.—The men advanced and sparred warily for a few moments, when Stanford exposed his cocoanut an instant, and Low struck out from the shoulder and split him in the mug. (Cries of "Bully for the Fat Boy!")

Fifth Round.—Stanford came up looking wicked, and let drive a heavy blow with his larboard flipper which caved in the side of his adversary's head. (Exclamations of "Hi! at him again Old Rusty!")

From this time until the end of the conflict, there was nothing regular in the proceedings. The two champions got furiously angry, and used up each other thus:

No sooner did Low realize that the side of his head was crushed in like a dent in a plug hat, than he "went after" Stanford in the most desperate manner. With one blow of his fist he mashed his nose so far into his face that a cavity was left in its place the size and shape of an ordinary soup-bowl. It is scarcely necessary to mention that in making room for so much nose, Gov. Stanford's eyes were crowded to such a degree as to cause them to "bug out" like a grasshopper's. His face was so altered that he scarcely looked like himself at all.

I never saw such a murderous expression as Stanford's countenance now assumed; you see it was so concentrated —it had such a small number of features to spread around over. He let fly one of his battering rams and caved in the other side of Low's head. Ah me, the latter was a ghastly sight to contemplate after that—one of the boys said it looked "like a beet which somebody had trod on it."

Low was "grit" though. He dashed out with his right and stove Stanford's chin clear back even with his ears. Oh, what a horrible sight he was, gasping and reaching after his tobacco, which was away back among his under-jaw teeth.

Stanford was unsettled for a while, but he soon rallied, and watching his chance, aimed a tremendous blow at his favorite mark, which crushed in the rear of Gov. Low's head in such a way that the crown thereof projected over his spinal column like a shed.

He came up to the scratch like a man, though, and sent one of his ponderous fists crashing through his opponent's ribs and in among his vitals, and instantly afterward he hauled out poor Stanford's left lung and smacked him in the face with it.

If I ever saw an angry man in my life it was Leland Stanford. He fairly raved. He jumped at his old speciality, Gov. Low's head; he tore it loose from his body and knocked him down with it. (Sensation in the crowd.)

Staggered by his extraordinary exertion, Gov. Stanford reeled, and before he could recover himself the headless but indomitable Low sprang forward, pulled one of his legs out by the roots, and dealt him a smashing paster over the eye with the end of it. The ever watchful Bill Stewart sallied out to the assistance of his crippled principal with a pair of crutches, and the battle went on again as fiercely as ever.

At this stage of the game the battle ground was strewn with a sufficiency of human remains to furnish material for the construction of three or four men of ordinary size, and good sound brains enough to stock a whole county like the one I came from in the noble old state of Missouri. And so dyed were the combatants in their own gore that they looked like shapeless, mutilated, red-shirted firemen.

The moment a chance offered, Low grabbed Stanford by the hair of the head, swung him thrice round and round in the air like a lasso, and then slammed him on the ground with such mighty force that he quivered all over, and squirmed painfully, like a worm; and behold, his body and such of his limbs as he had left, shortly assumed a swollen aspect like unto those of a rag doll-baby stuffed with saw-dust.

He rallied again, however, and the two desperadoes clinched and never let up until they had minced each other into such insignificant odds and ends that neither was able to distinguish his own remnants from those of his antagonist. It was awful.

Bill Stewart and Judge Field issued from their corners and gazed upon the sanguinary reminiscences in silence during several minutes. At the end of that time, having failed to discover that either champion had got the best of the fight, they threw up their sponges simultaneously, and Gen. Wright proclaimed in a loud voice that the battle was "drawn." May my ears never again be rent asunder with a burst of sound similar to that which greeted this announcement, from the multitudes. Amen.

By order of Gen. Wright, baskets were procured, and Bill Stewart and Judge Field proceeded to gather up the fragments of their late principals, while I gathered up my notes and went after my infernal horse, who had slipped his blankets and was foraging among the neighboring children. I—

P. S.—Messrs. Editors, I have been the victim of an infamous hoax. I have been imposed upon by that ponderous miscreant, Mr. Frank Lawler, of the Lick House. I left my room a moment ago, and the first man I met on the stairs was Gov. Stanford, alive and well, and as free from mutilation as you or I. I was speechless. Before I reached the street, I actually met Gov. Low also, with his own head on his own shoulders, his limbs intact, his inner mechanism in its proper place, and his cheeks blooming with gorgeous robustitude. I was amazed. But a word of explanation from him convinced me that I had been swindled by Mr. Lawler with a detail account of a fight which had never occurred, and was never likely to occur; that I had believed him so implicitly as to sit down and write it out (as other reporters have done before me) in language calculated to deceive the public into the conviction that I was present at it myself, and to embellish it with a string of falsehoods intended to render that deception as plausible as possible. I ruminated upon my singular position for many minutes, arrived at no conclusion—that is to say, no satisfactory conclusion, except that Lawler was an accomplished knave and I was a consummate ass. I had suspected the first before, though, and been acquainted with the latter fact for nearly a quarter of a century.

In conclusion, permit me to apologize in the most abject manner to the present Governor of California, to Hon. Mr. Low, the Governor elect, to Judge Field and to Hon. Wm. M. Stewart, for the great wrong which my natural imbecility has impelled me to do them in penning and publishing the foregoing sanguinary absurdity. If it were to do over again, I don't really know that I would do it. It is not possible for me to say how I ever managed to believe that refined and educated gentlemen like these could stoop to engage in the loathsome and degrading pastime of prize-fighting. It was just Lawler's work, you understand—the lubberly, swelled up effigy of a nine-days drowned man! But I shall get even with him for this. The only excuse he offers is that he got the story from John B. Winters, and thought of course it must be just so—as if a future Congressman for the state of Washoe could by any possibility tell the truth! Do you know that if either of these miserable scoundrels were to cross my path while I am in this mood I would scalp him in a minute? That's me—that's my style.

A CONCORD LOVE-SONG

BY JAMES JEFFREY ROCHE

Shall we meet again, love,
In the distant When, love,
When the Now is Then, love,
    And the Present Past?
Shall the mystic Yonder,
On which I ponder,
I sadly wonder,
    With thee be cast?

Ah, the joyless fleeting
Of our primal meeting,
And the fateful greeting
    Of the How and Why!
Ah, the Thingness flying
From the Hereness, sighing
For a love undying
    That fain would die!

Ah, the Ifness sadd'ning,
The Whichness madd'ning,
And the But ungladd'ning,
    That lie behind!
When the signless token
Of love is broken
In the speech unspoken
    Of mind to mind!

1913

A CONCORD LOVE-SONG

But the mind perceiveth
When the spirit grieveth,
And the heart relieveth
  Itself of woe;
And the doubt-mists lifted
From the eyes love-gifted
Are rent and rifted
  In the warmer glow.

In the inner Me, love,
As I turn to thee, love,
I seem to see, love,
  No Ego there.
But the Meness dead, love,
The Theeness fled, love,
And born instead, love,
  An Usness rare!

1914

THE MEETING

BY S. E. KISER

One day, in Paradise,
   Two angels, beaming, strolled
Along the amber walk that lies
   Beside the street of gold.

At last they met and gazed
   Into each other's eyes,
Then dropped their harps, amazed,
   And stood in mute surprise.

And other angels came,
   And, as they lingered near,
Heard both at once exclaim:
   "Say, how did you get here?"

1915

"THERE'S A BOWER OF BEAN-VINES"

BY PHŒBE CARY

There's a bower of bean-vines in Benjamin's yard,
    And the cabbages grow round it, planted for greens;
In the time of my childhood 'twas terribly hard
    To bend down the bean-poles, and pick off the beans.

That bower and its products I never forget,
    But oft, when my landlady presses me hard,
I think, are the cabbages growing there yet,
    Are the bean-vines still bearing in Benjamin's yard?

No, the bean-vines soon withered that once used to
        wave,
    But some beans had been gathered, the last that
        hung on;
And a soup was distilled in a kettle, that gave
    All the fragrance of summer when summer was
        gone.

Thus memory draws from delight, ere it dies,
    An essence that breathes of it awfully hard;
As thus good to my taste as 'twas then to my eyes,
    Is that bower of bean-vines in Benjamin's yard.

1916

THE TRIAL THAT JOB MISSED

BY KENNETT HARRIS

Job had troubles, I admit;
   Clearly was his patience shown,
Yet he never had to sit
   Waiting at the telephone—
Waiting, waiting to connect,
   The receiver at his lobe.
That's a trial, I expect,
   Would have been too much for Job!

After minutes of delay,
   While the cramps attacked his knees,
Then to hear Miss Central say
   Innocently: "Number, please!"
When the same he'd shouted out
   Twenty times—he'd rend his robe,
Tear his hair, I've little doubt;
   'Twould have been too much for Job.

Job, with all the woes he bore,
   Never got the "busy" buzz
When he tempted was of yore
   In the ancient land of Uz.
Satan missed it when he sought
   His one tender spot to probe;
If of "central" he had thought,
   She'd have been too much for Job!

1917

THE EVIDENCE IN THE CASE OF SMITH VS. JONES

BY SAMUEL L. CLEMENS

I reported this trial simply for my own amusement, one idle day last week, and without expecting to publish any portion of it—but I have seen the facts in the case so distorted and misrepresented in the daily papers that I feel it my duty to come forward and do what I can to set the plaintiff and defendant right before the public. This can best be done by submitting the plain, unembellished statements of the witnesses as given under oath before his Honor Judge Sheperd, in the Police Court, and leaving the people to form their own judgment of the matters involved, unbiased by argument or suggestion of any kind from me.

There is that nice sense of justice and that ability to discriminate between right and wrong, among the masses, which will enable them, after carefully reading the testimony I am about to set down here, to decide without hesitation which is the innocent party and which the guilty in the remarkable case of Smith vs. Jones, and I have every confidence that before this paper shall have been out of the printing-press twenty-four hours, the high court of The People, from whose decision there is no appeal, will have swept from the innocent man all taint of blame or suspicion, and cast upon the guilty one a deathless infamy.

To such as are not used to visiting the Police Court, I

will observe that there is nothing inviting about the place, there being no rich carpets, no mirrors, no pictures, no elegant sofa or arm-chairs to lounge in, no free lunch— and, in fact, nothing to make a man who has been there once desire to go again—except in cases where his bail is heavier than his fine is likely to be, under which circumstances he naturally has a tendency in that direction again, of course, in order to recover the difference.

There is a pulpit at the head of the hall, occupied by a handsome gray-haired judge, with a faculty of appearing pleasant and impartial to the disinterested spectator, and prejudiced and frosty to the last degree to the prisoner at the bar.

To the left of the pulpit is a long table for reporters; in front of the pulpit the clerks are stationed, and in the centre of the hall a nest of lawyers. On the left again are pine benches behind a railing, occupied by seedy white men, negroes, Chinamen, Kanakas—in a word, by the seedy and dejected of all nations—and in a corner is a box where more can be had when they are wanted.

On the right are more pine benches, for the use of prisoners, and their friends and witnesses.

An officer, in a gray uniform, and with a star upon his breast, guards the door.

A holy calm pervades the scene.

The case of Smith vs. Jones being called, each of these parties (stepping out from among the other seedy ones) gave the court a particular and circumstantial account of how the whole thing occurred, and then sat down.

The two narratives differed from each other.

In reality, I was half persuaded that these men were talking about two separate and distinct affairs altogether, inasmuch as no single circumstance mentioned by one was even remotely hinted at by the other.

Mr. Alfred Sowerby was then called to the witness-stand, and testified as follows:

"I was in the saloon at the time, your Honor, and I see this man Smith come up all of a sudden to Jones, who warn't saying a word, and split him in the snoot—"

LAWYER.—"Did what, sir?"

WITNESS.—"Busted him in the snoot."

LAWYER.—"What do you mean by such language as that? When you say that the plaintiff suddenly approached the defendant, who was silent at the time, and 'busted him in the snoot,' do you mean that the plaintiff struck the defendant?"

WITNESS.—"That's me—I'm swearing to that very circumstance—yes, your Honor, that was just the way of it. Now, for instance, as if you was Jones and I was Smith. Well, I comes up all of a sudden and says I to your Honor, says I, 'D—n your old tripe—' "

(Suppressed laughter in the lobbies.)

THE COURT.—"Order in the court! Witness, you will confine yourself to a plain statement of the facts in this case, and refrain from the embellishments of metaphor and allegory as far as possible."

WITNESS.—(Considerably subdued.)—"I beg your Honor's pardon—I didn't mean to be so brash. Well, Smith comes up to Jones all of a sudden and mashed him in the bugle—"

LAWYER.—"Stop! Witness, this kind of language will not do. I will ask you a plain question, and I require you to answer it simply, yes or no. Did—the—plaintiff—strike—the defendant? Did he strike him?"

WITNESS.—"You bet your sweet life he did. Gad! he gave him a paster in the trumpet—"

LAWYER.—"Take the witness! take the witness! take the witness! I have no further use for him."

The lawyer on the other side said he would endeavor to worry along without more assistance from Mr. Sowerby, and the witness retired to a neighboring bench.

Mr. McWilliamson was next called, and deposed as follows:

"I was a-standing as close to Mr. Smith as I am to this pulpit, a-chaffing with one of the lager beer girls—Sophronia by name, being from summers in Germany, so she says, but as to that, I—"

LAWYER.—"Well, now, never mind the nativity of the lager beer girl, but state, as concisely as possible, what you know of the assault and battery."

WITNESS.—"Certainly—certainly. Well, German or no German,—which I'll take my oath I don't believe she is, being of a red-headed disposition, with long, bony fingers, and no more hankering after Limberger cheese than—"

LAWYER.—"Stop that driveling nonsense and stick to the assault and battery. Go on with your story."

WITNESS.—"Well, sir, she—that is, Jones—he sidled up and drawed his revolver and tried to shoot the top of Smith's head off, and Smith run, and Sophronia she walloped herself down in the saw-dust and screamed twice, just as loud as she could yell. I never see a poor creature in such distress—and then she sung out: 'O, H—ll's fire! What are they up to now? Ah, my poor dear mother, I shall never see you more!'—saying which, she jerked another yell and fainted away as dead as a wax figger. Thinks I to myself, I'll be danged if this ain't gettin' rather dusty, and I'll—"

THE COURT.—"We have no desire to know what you thought; we only wish to know what you saw. Are you sure Mr. Jones endeavored to shoot the top of Mr. Smith's head off?"

WITNESS.—"Yes, your Honor."

THE COURT.—"How many times did he shoot?"

WITNESS.—"Well, sir, I couldn't say exactly as to the number—but I should think—well, say seven or eight times—as many as that, anyway."

THE COURT.—"Be careful now, and remember you are under oath. What kind of a pistol was it?"

WITNESS.—"It was a Durringer, your Honor."

THE COURT.—"A derringer! You must not trifle here, sir. A derringer only shoots once—how then could Jones have fired seven or eight times?" (The witness is evidently as stunned by that last proposition as if a brick had struck him.)

WITNESS.—"Well, your Honor—he—that is, she— Jones, I mean—Soph—"

THE COURT.—"Are you sure he fired more than one shot? Are you sure he fired at all?"

WITNESS.—"I—I well, perhaps he didn't—and—and your Honor may be right. But you see, that girl, with her dratted yowling—altogether, it might be that he did only shoot once."

LAWYER.—"And about his attempting to shoot the top of Smith's head off—didn't he aim at his body, or his legs? Come now."

WITNESS.—(Entirely confused)—"Yes, sir—I think he did—I—I'm pretty certain of it. Yes, sir, he must a fired at his legs."

(Nothing was elicited on the cross-examination, except that the weapon used by Mr. Jones was a bowie knife instead of a derringer, and that he made a number of desperate attempts to scalp the plaintiff instead of trying to shoot him. It also came out that Sophronia, of doubtful nativity, did not faint, and was not present during the affray, she having been discharged from her situation on the previous evening.)

Washington Billings, sworn, said: "I see the row, and it warn't in no saloon—it was in the street. Both of 'em was drunk, and one was a comin' up the street, and t'other was a goin' down. Both of 'em was close to the houses when they fust see each other, and both of 'em made their calculations to miss each other, but the second time they tacked across the pavement—driftin'-like, diagonal—they come together, down by curb—al-mighty soggy, they did—which staggered 'em a moment, and then, over they went, into the gutter. Smith was up fust, and he made a dive for a cobble and fell on Jones; Jones dug out and made a dive for a cobble, and slipped his hold and jammed his head into Smith's stomach. They each done that over again, twice more, just the same way. After that, neither of 'em could get up any more, and so they just laid there in the slush and clawed mud and cussed each other."

(On the cross-examination, the witness could not say whether the parties continued the fight afterward in the saloon or not—he only knew they began it in the gutter, and to the best of his knowledge and belief they were too drunk to get into a saloon, and too drunk to stay in it after they got there if there were any orifice about it that they could fall out again. As to weapons, he saw none used except the cobble-stones, and to the best of his knowledge and belief they missed fire every time while he was present.)

Jeremiah Driscoll came forward, was sworn, and testified as follows:—"I saw the fight, your Honor, and it wasn't in a saloon, nor in the street, nor in a hotel, nor in—"

THE COURT.—"Was it in the city and county of San Francisco!"

WITNESS.—"Yes, your Honor, I—I think it was."

THE COURT.—"Well, then, go on."

WITNESS.—"It was up in the Square. Jones meets Smith, and they both go at it—that is, blackguarding each other. One called the other a thief, and the other said he was a liar, and then they got to swearing backwards and forwards pretty generally, as you might say, and finally one struck the other over the head with a cane, and then they closed and fell, and after that they made such a dust and the gravel flew so thick that I couldn't rightly tell which was getting the best of it. When it cleared away, one of them was after the other with a pine bench, and the other was prospecting for rocks, and—"

LAWYER.—"There, there, there—that will do—that—will—do! How in the world is any one to make head or tail out of such a string of nonsense as that? Who struck the first blow?"

WITNESS.—"I can not rightly say, sir, but I think—"

LAWYER.—"You think!—don't you know?"

WITNESS.—"No, sir, it was all so sudden, and—"

LAWYER.—"Well, then, state, if you can, who struck the last."

WITNESS.—"I can't, sir, because—"

LAWYER.—"Because what?"

WITNESS.—"Because, sir, you see toward the last they clinched and went down, and got to kicking up the gravel again, and—"

LAWYER.—(Resignedly)—"Take the witness—take the witness."

(The testimony on the cross-examination went to show that during the fight, one of the parties drew a slung-shot and cocked it, but to the best of the witness' knowledge and belief, he did not fire; and at the same time, the other discharged a hand-grenade at his antagonist, which missed him and did no damage, except blowing up a bonnet store on the other side of the street, and creating a momentary diversion among the milliners. He could not say, however, which drew the slung-shot or which threw the grenade. (It was generally remarked by those in the court room, that the evidence of the witness was obscure and unsatisfactory. Upon questioning him further, and confronting him with the parties to the case before the court, it transpired that the faces of Jones and Smith were unknown to him, and that he had been talking about an entirely different fight all the time.)

Other witnesses were examined, some of whom swore that Smith was the aggressor, and others that Jones began the row; some said they fought with their fists, others that they fought with knives, others tomahawks, others revolvers, others clubs, others axes, others beer mugs and chairs, and others swore there had been no fight at all. However, fight or no fight, the testimony was straightforward and uniform on one point, at any rate, and that was, that the fuss was about two dollars and forty cents, which one party owed the other, but after all, it was impossible to find out which was the debtor and which the creditor.

After the witnesses had all been heard, his Honor, Judge Sheperd, observed that the evidence in this case resembled, in a great many points, the evidence before him in some thirty-five cases every day, on an average. He then said he would continue the case, to afford the parties an opportunity of procuring more testimony.

(I have been keeping an eye on the Police Court for the last few days. Two friends of mine had business there, on account of assault and battery concerning

Washoe stocks, and I felt interested, of course. I never knew their names were James Johnson and John Ward, though, until I heard them answer to them in that court. When James Johnson was called, one of these young men said to the other: "That's you, my boy." "No," was the reply, "it's you—my name's John Ward—see, I've got it written here on a card." Consequently, the first speaker sung out, "Here!" and it was all right. As I was saying, I have been keeping an eye on that court, and I have arrived at the conclusion that the office of Police Judge is a profitable and a comfortable thing to have, but then, as the English hunter said about fighting tigers in India under a shortness of ammunition, "It has its little drawbacks." Hearing testimony must be worrying to a Police Judge sometimes, when he is in his right mind. I would rather be secretary to a wealthy mining company, and have nothing to do but advertise the assessments and collect them in carefully, and go along quiet and upright, and be one of the noblest works of God, and never gobble a dollar that didn't belong to me—all just as those fellows do, you know. (Oh, I have no talent for sarcasm, it isn't likely.) But I trespass.

Now, with every confidence in the instinctive candor and fair dealing of my race, I submit the testimony in the case of Smith vs. Jones to the people, without comment or argument, well satisfied that after a perusal of it, their judgment will be as righteous as it is final and impartial, and that whether Smith be cast out and Jones exalted, or Jones cast out and Smith exalted, the decision will be a holy and a just one.

I leave the accused and the accuser before the bar of the world—let their fate be pronounced.

A DOUBLE-DYED DECEIVER

BY O. HENRY

I

The trouble began in Laredo. It was the Llano Kid's fault, for he should have confined his habit of manslaughter to Mexicans. But the Kid was past twenty; and to have only Mexicans to one's credit at twenty is to blush unseen on the Rio Grande border.

It happened in old Justo Valdos's gambling house. There was a poker game at which sat players who were not all friends, as happens often where men ride in from afar to shoot Folly as she gallops. There was a row over so small a matter as a pair of queens; and when the smoke had cleared away it was found that the Kid had committed an indiscretion, and his adversary had been guilty of a blunder. For, the unfortunate combatant, instead of being a Greaser, was a high-blooded youth from the cow ranches, of about the Kid's own age and possessed of friends and champions. His blunder in missing the Kid's right ear only a sixteenth of an inch when he pulled his gun did not lessen the indiscretion of the better marksman.

The Kid, not being equipped with a retinue, nor bountifully supplied with personal admirers and supporters—on account of a rather umbrageous reputation even for the border—considered it not incompatible with his indisputable gameness to perform that judicious tractional act known as "pulling his freight."

Quickly the avengers gathered and sought him. Three of them overtook him within a rod of the station. The Kid turned and showed his teeth in that brilliant but mirthless smile that usually preceded his deeds of insolence and violence, and his pursuers fell back without making it necessary for him even to reach for his weapon.

But in this affair the Kid had not felt the grim thirst for encounter that usually urged him on to battle. It had been a purely chance row, born of the cards and certain epithets impossible for a gentleman to brook, that had passed between the two. The Kid had rather liked the slim, haughty, brown-faced young chap whom his bullet had cut off in the first pride of manhood. And now he wanted no more blood. He wanted to get away and have a good long sleep somewhere in the sun on the mesquit grass with his handkerchief over his face. Even a Mexican might have crossed his path in safety while he was in this mood.

The Kid openly boarded the north-bound passenger-train that departed five minutes later. But at Webb, a few miles out, where it was flagged to take on a traveler, he abandoned that manner of escape. There were telegraph stations ahead; and the Kid looked askance at electricity and steam. Saddle and spur were his rocks of safety.

The man whom he had shot was a stranger to him. But the Kid knew that he was of the Corralitos outfit from Hidalgo; and that the punchers from that ranch were more relentless and vengeful than Kentucky feudists when wrong or harm was done to one of them. So, with the wisdom that has characterized many great fighters, the Kid decided to pile up as many leagues as possible of chaparral and pear between himself and the retaliation of the Corralitos bunch.

Near the station was a store; and near the store, scattered among the mesquits and elms, stood the saddled horses of the customers. Most of them waited, half asleep, with sagging limbs and drooping heads. But one, a long-legged roan with a curved neck, snorted and pawed the turf. Him the Kid mounted, gripped with his knees, and slapped gently with the owner's own quirt.

If the slaying of the temerarious card-player had cast a cloud over the Kid's standing as a good and true citizen, this last act of his veiled his figure in the darkest shadows of disrepute. On the Rio Grande border, if you take a man's life you sometimes take trash; but if you take his horse, you take a thing the loss of which renders him poor, indeed, and which enriches you not—if you are caught. For the Kid there was no turning back now.

With the springing roan under him he felt little care or uneasiness. After a five-mile gallop he drew in to the plainsman's jogging trot, and rode northeastward toward the Nueces River bottoms. He knew the country well— its most tortuous and obscure trails through the great wilderness of brush and pear, and its camps and lonesome ranches where one might find safe entertainment. Always he bore to the east; for the Kid had never seen the ocean, and he had a fancy to lay his hand upon the mane of the great Gulf, the gamesome colt of the greater waters.

So after three days he stood on the shore at Corpus Christi, and looked out across the gentle ripples of a quiet sea.

Captain Boone, of the schooner Flyaway, stood near his skiff, which one of his crew was guarding in the surf. When ready to sail he had discovered that one of the necessaries of life, in the parallelogrammatic shape of plug tobacco, had been forgotten. A sailor had been despatched for the missing cargo. Meanwhile the captain paced the sands, chewing profanely at his pocket store.

A slim, wiry youth in high-heeled boots came down to the water's edge. His face was boyish but with a premature severity that hinted at a man's experience. His complexion was naturally dark; and the sun and wind of an outdoor life had burned it to a coffee brown. His hair was as black and straight as an Indian's; his face had not yet been upturned to the humiliation of a razor; his eyes were a cold and steady blue. He carried his left arm somewhat away from his body, for pearl-handled .45s are frowned upon by town marshals, and are a little bulky when packed in the left armhole of one's vest. He looked beyond Captain Boone at the gulf with the impersonal and expressionless dignity of a Chinese emperor.

"Thinkin' of buyin' that 'ar gulf, buddy?" asked the captain, made sarcastic by his narrow escape from a tobaccoless voyage.

"Why, no," said the Kid gently, "I reckon not. I never saw it before. I was just looking at it. Not thinking of selling it, are you?"

"Not this trip," said the captain. "I'll send it to you C. O. D. when I get back to Buenas Tierras. Here comes that capstan-footed lubber with the chewin'. I ought to've weighed anchor an hour ago."

"Is that your ship out there?" asked the Kid.

"Why, yes," answered the captain, "if you want to call a schooner a ship, and I don't mind lyin'. But you better say Miller and Gonzales, owners, and ordinary, plain, Billy-be-damned old Samuel K. Boone, skipper."

"Where are you going to?" asked the refugee.

"Buenas Tierras, coast of South America—I forget what they called the country the last time I was there. Cargo—lumber, corrugated iron, and machetes."

"What kind of a country is it?" asked the Kid—"hot or cold?"

"Warmish, buddy," said the captain. "But a regular Paradise Lost for elegance of scenery and be-yooty of geography. Ye're wakened every morning by the sweet singin' of red birds with seven purple tails, and the sighin' of breezes in the posies and roses. And the inhabitants never work, for they can reach out and pick steamer baskets of the choicest hothouse fruit without gettin' out of bed. And there's no Sunday and no ice and no rent and no troubles and no use and no nothin'. It's a great country for a man to go to sleep with, and wait for somethin' to turn up. The bananys and oranges and hurricanes and pineapples that ye eat comes from there."

"That sounds to me!" said the Kid, at last betraying interest. "What'll the expressage be to take me out there with you?"

"Twenty-four dollars," said Captain Boone; "grub and transportation. Second cabin. I haven't got a first cabin."

"You've got my company," said the Kid, pulling out a buckskin bag.

With three hundred dollars he had gone to Laredo for his regular "blowout." The duel in Valdo's had cut short his season of hilarity, but it had left him with nearly $200 for aid in the flight that it had made necessary.

"All right, buddy," said the captain. "I hope your ma won't blame me for this little childish escapade of yours." He beckoned to one of the boat's crew. "Let Sanchez lift you out to the skiff so you won't get your feet wet."

II

Thacker, the United States consul at Buenas Tierras, was not yet drunk. It was only eleven o'clock; and he never arrived at his desired state of beatitude—a state wherein he sang ancient maudlin vaudeville songs and pelted his screaming parrot with banana peels—until the middle of the afternoon. So, when he looked up from his hammock at the sound of a slight cough, and saw the Kid standing in the door of the consulate, he was still in a condition to extend the hospitality and courtesy due from the representative of a great nation.

"Don't disturb yourself," said the Kid easily. "I just dropped in. They told me it was customary to light at your camp before starting in to round up the town. I just came in on a ship from Texas."

"Glad to see you, Mr. ——," said the consul.

The Kid laughed.

"Sprague Dalton," he said. "It sounds funny to me to hear it. I'm called the Llano Kid in the Rio Grande country."

"I'm Thacker," said the consul. "Take that cane-bottom chair. Now if you've come to invest, you want somebody to advise you. These dingies will cheat you out of the gold in your teeth if you don't understand their ways. Try a cigar?"

"Much obliged," said the Kid, "but if it wasn't for my corn shucks and the little bag in my back pocket, I couldn't live a minute." He took out his "makings," and rolled a cigarette.

"They speak Spanish here," said the consul. "You'll need an interpreter. If there's anything I can do, why, I'd be delighted. If you're buying fruit lands or looking for a concession of any sort, you'll want somebody who knows the ropes to look out for you."

"I speak Spanish," said the Kid, "about nine times better than I do English. Everybody speaks it on the range where I come from. And I'm not in the market for anything."

"You speak Spanish?" said Thacker thoughtfully. He regarded the Kid absorbedly.

"You look like a Spaniard, too," he continued. "And you're from Texas. And you can't be more than twenty or twenty-one. I wonder if you've got any nerve."

"You got a deal of some kind to put through?" asked the Texan, with unexpected shrewdness.

"Are you open to a proposition?" said Thacker.

"What's the use to deny it?" said the Kid. "I got into a little gun frolic down in Laredo and plugged a white man. There wasn't any Mexican handy. And I come down to your parrot-and-monkey range just for to smell the morning-glories and marigolds. Now, do you *sabe?*"

Thacker got up and closed the door.

"Let me see your hand," he said.

He took the Kid's left hand, and examined the back of it closely.

"I can do it," he said excitedly. "Your flesh is as hard as wood and as healthy as a baby's. It will heal in a week."

"If it's a fist fight you want to back me for," said the Kid, "don't put your money up yet. Make it gun work, and I'll keep you company. But no barehanded scrapping, like ladies at a tea-party, for me."

"It's easier than that," said Thacker. "Just step here, will you?"

Through the window he pointed to a two-story white-stuccoed house with wide galleries rising amid the deep green tropical foliage on a wooded hill that sloped gently from the sea.

"In that house," said Thacker, "a fine old Castilian gentleman and his wife are yearning to gather you into their arms and fill your pockets with money. Old Santos Urique lives there. He owns half the gold-mines in the country."

"You haven't been eating loco weed, have you?" asked the Kid.

"Sit down again," said Thacker, "and I'll tell you. Twelve years ago they lost a kid. No, he didn't die—although most of 'em here do from drinking the surface water. He was a wild little devil, even if he wasn't but eight years old. Everybody knows about it. Some Americans who were through here prospecting for gold had letters to Señor Urique, and the boy was a favorite with them. They filled his head with big stories about the States; and about a month after they left, the kid disappeared, too. He was supposed to have stowed himself away among the banana bunches on a fruit steamer, and gone to New Orleans. He was seen once afterward in Texas, it was thought, but they never heard anything more of him. Old Urique has spent thousands of dollars having him looked for. The madam was broken up worst of all. The kid was her life. She wears mourning yet. But they say she believes he'll come back to her some day, and never gives up hope. On the back of the boy's left hand was tattooed a flying eagle carrying a spear in his claws. That's old Urique's coat of arms or something that he inherited in Spain."

The Kid raised his left hand slowly and gazed at it curiously.

"That's it," said Thacker, reaching behind the official desk for his bottle of smuggled brandy. "You're not so slow. I can do it. What was I consul at Sandakan for? I never knew till now. In a week I'll have the eagle bird with the frog-sticker blended in so you'd think you were born with it. I brought a set of the needles and ink just because I was sure you'd drop in some day, Mr. Dalton."

"Oh, hell," said the Kid. "I thought I told you."

"All right, 'Kid,' then. It won't be that long. How does Señorito Urique sound, for a change?"

"I never played son any that I remember of," said the Kid. "If I had any parents to mention they went over the divide about the time I gave my first bleat. What is the plan of your round-up?"

Thacker leaned back against the wall and held his glass up to the light.

"We've come now," said he, "to the question of how far you're willing to go in a little matter of the sort."

"I told you why I came down here," said the Kid simply.

"A good answer," said the consul. "But you won't have to go that far. Here's the scheme. After I get the trade-mark tattooed on your hand I'll notify old Urique. In the meantime I'll furnish you with all of the family history I can find out, so you can be studying up points to talk about. You've got the looks, you speak the Spanish, you know the facts, you can tell about Texas, you've got the tattoo mark. When I notify them that the rightful heir has returned and is waiting to know whether he will be received and pardoned, what will happen? They'll simply rush down here and fall on your neck, and the curtain goes down for refreshments and a stroll in the lobby."

"I'm waiting," said the Kid. "I haven't had my saddle off in your camp long, pardner, and I never met you before; but if you intend to let it go at a parental blessing, why, I'm mistaken in my man, that's all."

"Thanks," said the consul. "I haven't met anybody in a long time that keeps up with an argument as well as you do. The rest of it is simple. If they take you in only for a while it's long enough. Don't give 'em time to hunt up the strawberry mark on your left shoulder. Old Urique keeps anywhere from $50,000 to $100,000 in his house all the time in a little safe that you could open with a shoe buttoner. Get it. My skill as a tattooer is worth half the boodle. We go halves and catch a tramp steamer for Rio Janeiro. Let the United States go to pieces if it can't get along without my services. *Que dice, señor?*"

"It sounds to me!" said the Kid, nodding his head. "I'm out for the dust."

"All right, then," said Thacker. "You'll have to keep close until we get the bird on you. You can live in the back room here. I do my own cooking, and I'll make you as comfortable as a parsimonious Government will allow me."

Thacker had set the time at a week, but it was two weeks before the design that he patiently tattooed upon the Kid's hand was to his notion. And then Thacker called a *muchacho,* and despatched this note to the intended victim:

El Senor Don Santos Urique,
   La Casa Blanca.
My Dear Sir: I beg permission to inform you that there is in my house as a temporary guest a young man who arrived in Buenas Tierras from the United States some days ago. Without wishing to excite any hopes that may not be realized, I think there is a possibility of his being your long-absent son. It might be well for you to call and see him. If he is, it is my opinion that his intention was to return to his home, but upon arriving here, his courage failed him from doubts as to how he would be received.   Your true servant,
                            Thompson Thacker.

Half an hour afterward—quick time for Buenas
Tierras—Señor Urique's ancient landau drove to the consul's door, with the barefooted coachman beating and
shouting at the team of fat, awkward horses.

A tall man with a white mustache alighted, and assisted
to the ground a lady who was dressed and veiled in unre-
lieved black.

The two hastened inside, and were met by Thacker with
his best diplomatic bow. By his desk stood a slender
young man with clear-cut, sun-browned features and
smoothly brushed black hair.

Señora Urique threw back her heavy veil with a quick
gesture. She was past middle age, and her hair was beginning to silver, but her full, proud figure and clear olive
skin retained traces of the beauty peculiar to the Basque
province. But, once you had seen her eyes, and compre-
hended the great sadness that was revealed in their deep
shadows and hopeless expression, you saw that the woman lived only in some memory.

She bent upon the young man a long look of the most
agonized questioning. Then her great black eyes turned,
and her gaze rested upon his left hand. And then with a
sob, not loud, but seeming to shake the room, she cried
"Hijo mio!" and caught the Llano Kid to her heart.

III

A month afterward the Kid came to the consulate in
response to a message sent by Thacker.

He looked the young Spanish *caballero*. His clothes
were imported, and the wiles of the jewelers had not been
spent upon him in vain. A more than respectable diamond shone on his finger as he rolled a shuck cigarette.

"What's doing?" asked Thacker.

1937

"Nothing much," said the Kid calmly. "I eat my first iguana steak to-day. They're them big lizards, you *sabe?* I reckon, though, that frijoles and side bacon would do me about as well. Do you care for iguanas, Thacker?"

"No, nor for some other kinds of reptiles," said Thacker.

It was three in the afternoon, and in another hour he would be in his state of beatitude.

"It's time you were making good, sonny," he went on, with an ugly look on his reddened face. "You're not playing up to me square. You've been the prodigal son for four weeks now, and you could have had veal for every meal on a gold dish if you'd wanted it. Now, Mr. Kid, do you think it's right to leave me out so long on a husk diet? What's the trouble? Don't you get your filial eyes on anything that looks like cash in the Casa Blanca? Don't tell me you don't. Everybody knows where old Urique keeps his stuff. It's U. S. currency, too; he don't accept anything else. What's doing? Don't say 'nothing' this time."

"Why, sure," said the Kid, admiring his diamond, "there's plenty of money up there. I'm no judge of collateral in bunches, but I will undertake for to say that I've seen the rise of $50,000 at a time in that tin grub box that my adopted father calls his safe. And he lets me carry the key sometimes just to show me that he knows I'm the real little Francisco that strayed from the herd a long time ago."

"Well, what are you waiting for?" asked Thacker angrily. "Don't you forget that I can upset your apple cart any day I want to. If old Urique knew you were an impostor, what sort of things would happen to you? Oh, you don't know this country, Mr. Texas Kid. The laws here have got mustard spread between 'em. These people here'd stretch you out like a frog that had been stepped on, and give you about fifty sticks at every corner of the plaza. And they'd wear every stick out, too. What was left of you they'd feed to alligators."

"I might as well tell you now, pardner," said the Kid, sliding down low on his steamer chair, "that things are going to stay just as they are. They're about right now."

"What do you mean?" asked Thacker, rattling the bottom of his glass on his desk.

"The scheme's off," said the Kid. "And whenever you have the pleasure of speaking to me address me as Don Francisco Urique. I'll guarantee I'll answer to it. We'll let Colonel Urique keep his money. His little tin safe is as good as the time-locker in the First National Bank of Laredo as far as you and me are concerned."

"You're going to throw me down, then, are you?" said the consul.

"Sure," said the Kid cheerfully. "Throw you down. That's it. And now I'll tell you why. The first night I was up at the colonel's house they introduced me to a bedroom. No blankets on the floor—a real room, with a bed and things in it. And before I was asleep, in comes this artificial mother of mine and tucks in the covers. 'Panchito,' she says, 'my little lost one, God has brought you back to me. I bless his name forever.' It was that, or some truck like that, she said. And down comes a drop or two of rain and hits me on the nose. And all that stuck by me, Mr. Thacker. And it's been that way ever since. And it's got to stay that way. Don't you think that it's for what's in it for me, either, that I say so. If you have any such ideas, keep 'em to yourself. I haven't had much truck with women in my life, and no mothers to speak of, but here's a lady that we've got to keep fooled. Once she stood it; twice she won't. I'm a low-down wolf, and the devil may have sent me on this trail instead of God, but I'll travel it to the end. And now, don't forget that I'm Don Francisco Urique whenever you happen to mention my name."

"I'll expose you to-day, you—you double-dyed traitor," stammered Thacker.

The Kid arose and, without violence, took Thacker by the throat with a hand of steel, and shoved him slowly into a corner. Then he drew from under his left arm his pearl-handled .45 and poked the cold muzzle of it against the consul's mouth.

"I told you why I come here," he said, with his old freezing smile. "If I leave here, you'll be the reason. Never forget it, pardner. Now, what is my name?"

"Er—Don Francisco Urique," gasped Thacker.

From outside came a sound of wheels, and the shouting of some one, and the sharp thwacks of a wooden whip-stock upon the backs of fat horses.

The Kid put up his gun, and walked toward the door. But he turned again and came back to the trembling Thacker, and help up his left hand with its back toward the consul.

"There's one more reason," he said slowly, "why things have got to stand as they are. The fellow I killed in Laredo had one of them same pictures on his left hand."

Outside, the ancient landau of Don Santos Urique rattled to the door. The coachman ceased his bellowing. Señora Urique, in a voluminous gay gown of white lace and flying ribbons, leaned forward with a happy look in her great soft eyes.

"Are you within, dear son?" she called, in the rippling Castilian.

"*Madre mio, yo vengo* [mother, I come]," answered the young Don Francisco Urique.

AN OLD-TIME SINGER

BY FRANK L. STANTON

I don't want any hymnbook when the Methodists is nigh,
A-linin' out the ol' ones that went thrillin' to the sky
In the ol' campmeetin' seasons, when 'twuz "Glory hal-
lelu!"
An' "Brother, rise an' tell us what the Lord has done fer
you!"

Fer I know them songs so perfect that when I git the
swing
O' the tune they want to go to I kin shet my eyes an' sing!
"On Jordan's stormy banks," an' ol' "Amazin' Grace"—
they seem
So nat'ral, I'm like some one that's singin' in a dream!

Oh, when it comes to them ol' songs I allus does my part;
An' I've got the ol'-time Bible down, as you might say,
"by heart!"
When the preacher says the fust word in the givin' of his
text
I smile with satisfaction, kaze I know what's comin' next!

The wife says: "That's amazin'!" an' the preacher says
—says he,
With lots o' meanin' in his voice, an' lookin' queer at
me—

"Sence you know more o' the Bible than the best o' us kin
      teach,
Don't you think you orter practice what you're payin' us
      to preach?"

Well, *that* gits me in a *corner*—an' I sorter raise my eyes
An' the tune about them titles to the "mansions in the
      skies"!
I want the benediction then—I'm ready to depart!
But when it comes to singin'—well, I've got the hymns
      by heart!

1942

BREITMANN IN POLITICS

Showing How Mr. Hiram Twine "Played Off" on Smith

BY CHARLES GODFREY LELAND

Vide licet: Dere vas a fillage
    Whose vode alone vouldt pe
Apout enoof to elegdt a man,
    Und gife a mayority;
So de von who couldt scoop dis seddlement
    Vould make a pully hit;
Boot dough dey vere Deutschers, von und all,
    Dey all go von on Schmit.

Now it happenet to gome to bass
    Dat in dis liddle town
De Deutsch vas all exshpegdin
    Dat Mishder Schmit coom down,
His brinciples to fore-setzen
    Und his ideés to deach,
(Dat is, fix oop de brifate pargains)
    Und telifer a pooblic sbeech.

Now Twine vas a gyrotwistive cuss,
    Ash blainly ish peen shown,
Und vas alfays an out-findin
    Votefer might pe known;
Und mit some of his circumswindles
    He fix de matter so
Dat he'd pe himself at dis meetin
    And see how dings vas go.

1943

Oh shtrangely in dis leben
  De dings kits vorked apout!
Oh voonderly Fortuna
  Makes toorn us insite out!
Oh sinkular de luck-wheel rolls!
  Dis liddle meeding dere
Fixt Twine *ad perpendiculum*—
  Shoost suit him to a hair!

Now it hoppenit on dis efenin
  De Deutschers, von und all,
Vere avaitin mit impatience
  De openin of de ball;
Und de shates of nite vere fallin
  Und de shdars begin to plink,
Und dey vish dat Schmit vouldt hoorry,
  For 'dvas dime to dake a trink.

Dey hear some hoofs a-dramplin,
  Und dey saw, und dinked dey knowed,
Der bretty greature coomin,
  On his horse along de road;
Und ash he ride town in-ward
  De likeness vas so plain
Dey donnered out, "Hooray for Schmit!"
  Enough to make it rain.

Der Twine vas shtart like plazes;
  Boot oopshtarted too his wit,
Und he dinks, "Great Turnips! what if I
  Could bass for Colonel Schmit?
Gaul dern my heels! *I'll do it*,
  Und go the total swine!
Oh, Soap-balls! what a chance!" said dis
  Dissembulatin Twine.

1944

Den 'twas "Willkomm! willkomm, Mishder
    Schmit!"
  Ringsroom on efery site;
Und "First-rate! How dy-do yourself?"
  Der Hiram Twine replied.
Dey ashk him, "Come und dake a trink?"
  But dey find it mighdy queer
Ven Twine informs dem none boot hogs
  Vould trink dat shtinkin bier;

Dat all lager vas nodings boot boison;
  Und ash for Sherman wein,
He dinks it vas erfounden
  Exshbressly for Sherman schwein;
Dat he himself vas a demperanceler—
  Dat he gloria in de name;
Und atfise dem all, for tecency's sake,
  To go und do de same.

Dese bemarks among de Deutschers
  Vere apout ash vell receife
Ash a cats in a game of den-bins,
  Ash you may of coorse peliefe:
De heat of de reception
  Vent down a dootzen tegrees,
Und in place of hurraws dere vas only heardt
  De rooslin of de drees.

Und so in solemn stille
  Dey scorched him to de hall,
Vhere he maket de oradion
  Vitch vas so moosh to blease dem all;
Und dis vay he pegin it:
  "Pefore I furder go,
I vish dat my obinions
  You puddin-het Dootch should know.

1945

"Und ere I norate to you,
 I think it only fair
We should oonderstand each other
 Prezactly, chunk and square.
Dere are boints on vhich ve tisagree,
 And I will plank de facts—
I don't go round slanganderin
 My friendts pehind deir packs.

"So I beg you dake it easy
 If on de raw I touch,
Vhen I say I can't apide de sound
 Of your groontin, shi-shing Dutch.
Should I in the Legisladure
 As your slumgullion shtand,
I'll have a bill forbidding Dutch
 Troo all dis 'versal land.

"Should a husband talk it to his frau,
 To deat' he should pe led;
If a mutter breat' it to her shild,
 I'd bunch her in de head;
Und I'm sure dat none vill atfocate
 Ids use in public schools,
Oonless dey're peastly, nashdy, prutal,
 Sauerkraut-eaten vools."

Here Mishder Twine, to gadder breat,
 Shoost make a liddle pause,
Und see sechs hundert gapin eyes,
 Sechs hundert shdarin chaws,
Dey shtanden erstarrt like frozen;
 Von faindly dried to hiss;
Und von set: "Ish it shleeps I'm treamin?
 Gottausend! vat ish dis?"

1946

CHARLES GODFREY LELAND

Twine keptet von eye on de vindow,
  Boot poldly went ahet:
"Of your oder shtinkin hobits
  No vordt needt hier pe set.
Shtop goozlin bier—shtop shmokin bipes—
  Shtop rootin in de mire;
Und shoost *un-Dutchify* yourselfs:
  Dat's all dat I require."

Und *denn* dere coomed a shindy,
  Ash if de shky hat trop:
"Trow him mit ecks, py doonder!
  Go shlog him on de kop!
Hei! Shoot him mit a powie-knifes;
  Go for him, ganz and gar!
Shoost tar him mit some fedders!
  Led's fedder him mit tar!"

Sooch a teufel's row of furie
  Vas nefer oop-kickt before:
Soom roosh to on-climb de blatform—
  Soom hoory to fasten te toor:
Von veller vired his refolfer,
  Boot de pullet missed her mark:
She coot de cort of de shandelier:
  It vell, und de hall vas tark!

Oh, vell was it for Hiram Twine
  Dat nimply he couldt shoomp;
Und vell dat he light on a misthauf,
  Und nefer feel de boomp;
Und vell for him dat his goot cray horse
  Shtood sattled shoost outside;
Und vell dat in an augenblick
  He vas off on a teufel's ride.

1947

Bang! bang! de sharp pistolen shots
　Vent pipin py his ear,
Boot he tortled oop de barrick road
　Like any mountain deer:
Dey trowed der Hiram Twine mit shteins,
　But dey only could be-mark
Von climpse of his vhite obercoadt,
　Und a clotterin in de tark.

So dey all versembled togeder,
　Ein ander to sprechen mit,
Und allow dat sooch a rede
　Dey nefer exshpegd from Schmit—
Dat he vas a foorst-glass plackguard,
　And so pig a Lump ash ran;
So, *nemine contradicente,*
　Dey vented for Breitmann.

Und 'twas annerthalb yar dereafter
　Before der Schmit vas know
Vot maket dis rural fillage
　Go pack oopon him so;
Und he schvored at de Dootch more schlimmer
　Ash Hiram Twine had tone.
Nota bene: He tid it in earnesht,
　Vhile der Hiram's vas pusiness fun.

Boot vhen Breitmann heard de shdory,
　How de fillage hat peen dricked,
He shvore bei Leib und Leben
　He'd rader hafe been licked
Dan be helped bei sooch shumgoozlin;
　Und 'twas petter to pe a schwein
Dan a schwindlin honeyfooglin shnake,
　Like dat lyin Yankee Twine.

1948

Und pegot so heafy disgoosted
  Mit de boledicks of dis land,
Dat his friendts couldn't barely keep him
  From trowin oop his hand,
Vhen he helt shtraidt flush, mit an ace in his
      poot;
  Vich phrase ish all de same,
In de science of de pokerology,
  Ash if he got de game.

So Breitmann cot elegtet,
  Py vollowin de vay
Dey manage de elegdions
  Unto dis fery day;
Vitch shows de Deutsch *Dummehrlichkeit,*
  Also de Yankee "wit":
Das ist Abenteuer
  How Breitmann lick der Schmit.

1949

LOVE SONG

BY CHARLES GODFREY LELAND

Overe mine lofe a sugar-powl,
  De fery shmallest loomp
Vouldt shveet de seas from bole to bole,
  Und make de shildren shoomp.
Und if she vere a clofer-fieldt,
  I'd bet mine only pence,
It vouldn't pe no dime at all
  Pefore I'd shoomp de fence.

Her heafenly foice it drill me so,
  It really seems to hoort;
She ish de holiest anamile
  Dat roons oopon de dirt.
De re'nbow rises ven she sings,
  De sonn shine ven she dalk,
De angels crow und flop deir vings
  Ven she goes out to valk.

So livin vhite—so carnadine—
  Mine lofe's gomblexion glow;
It's shoost like abendcarmosine
  Rich gleamin on de shnow.
Her soul makes plooshes in her sheek,
  As sommer reds de wein,
Or sonlight sends a fire-life troo
  An blank karfunkelstein.

1950

De ueberschwengliche idées
  Dis lofe put in my mind,
Vould make a foostrate philosoph
  Of any human kind.
'Tis shuderned sweet on eart' to meet
  An himmlisch-hoellisch qual,
Und treat mit whiles to kümmel schnapps
  De Shœnheitsideál.

1951

CONTENTMENT

"Man wants but little here below"

BY OLIVER WENDELL HOLMES

Little I ask; my wants are few;
   I only wish a hut of stone,
(A *very plain* brownstone will do,)
   That I may call my own;—
And close at hand is such a one,
In yonder street that fronts the sun.

Plain food is quite enough for me;
   Three courses are as good as ten;—
If Nature can subsist on three,
   Thank Heaven for three.   Amen!
I always thought cold victual nice;—
My *choice* would be vanilla-ice.

I care not much for gold or land;—
   Give me a mortgage here and there,—
Some good bank-stock, some note of hand,
   Or trifling railroad share,—
I only ask that Fortune send
A *little* more than I shall spend.

Honors are silly toys, I know,
   And titles are but empty names;
I would, *perhaps,* be Plenipo,—
   But only near St. James;
I'm very sure I should not care
To fill our Gubernator's chair.

1952

Jewels are bawbles; 'tis a sin
  To care for such unfruitful things;—
One good-sized diamond in a pin,—
  Some, *not so large,* in rings,—
A ruby, and a pearl, or so,
Will do for me;—I laugh at show.

My dame should dress in cheap attire;
  (Good, heavy silks are never dear;)—
I own perhaps I *might* desire
  Some shawls of true Cashmere,—
Some marrowy crapes of China silk,
Like wrinkled skins on scalded milk.

I would not have the horse I drive
  So fast that folks must stop and stare;
An easy gait—two, forty-five—
  Suits me; I do not care;—
Perhaps, for just a *single spurt,*
Some seconds less would do no hurt.

Of pictures, I should like to own
  Titians and Raphaels three or four,—
I love so much their style and tone,—
  One Turner, and no more,
(A landscape,—foreground golden dirt,—
The sunshine painted with a squirt.)

Of books but few,—some fifty score
  For daily use, and bound for wear;
The rest upon an upper floor;—
  Some *little* luxury *there*
Of red morocco's gilded gleam,
And vellum rich as country cream.

1953

CONTENTMENT

Busts, cameos, gems,—such things as these,
　　Which others often show for pride,
I value for their power to please,
　　And selfish churls deride;—
One Stradivarius, I confess,
Two Meerschaums, I would fain possess.

Wealth's wasteful tricks I will not learn
　　Nor ape the glittering upstart fool;—
Shall not carved tables serve my turn,
　　But *all* must be of buhl?
Give grasping pomp its double share,—
I ask but *one* recumbent chair.

Thus humble let me live and die,
　　Nor long for Midas' golden touch;
If Heaven more generous gifts deny,
　　I shall not miss them *much,*—
Too grateful for the blessing lent
Of simple tastes and mind content!

TOM'S MONEY

BY HARRIET PRESCOTT SPOFFORD

Mrs. Laughton had found what she had been looking
for all her life—the man under her bed.

Every night of her nearly thirty years of existence this
pretty little person had stooped on her knees, before saying her prayers, and had investigated the space beneath
her bed, a light brass affair, hung with a chintz valance;
had then peered beneath the dark recess of the dressing-
case, and having looked in the deep drawer of the bureau
and into the closet, she fastened her door and felt as se-
cure as a snail in a shell. As she never, in this particular
business, seemed to have any confidence in Mr. Laughton,
in spite of the fact that she admired him and adored him,
neither his presence nor his absence ever made any varia-
tion in the performance. She had gone through the motions, however, for so long a time that they had come to
be in a manner perfunctory, and the start she received on
this night of which I speak made her prayers quite impossible.

What was she to do? She, a coward *par eminence,*
known to be the most timorous of the whole family; her
tremors at all sorts of imagined dangers affording laughter to the flock of sisters and brothers. Should she stay
on her knees after having seen that dark shape, as if
going on with her prayers, while revolving some plan of
procedure? That was out of the question. Scream? She
couldn't have screamed to save her life. Run? She could
no more have set one foot before the other, than if her

body had melted from the waist down. She was deadly faint and cold and shaking, and all in a second, in the fraction of a second, before she had risen from her stooping posture.

Oh, why wasn't it Virginia instead? Virginia had always had such heroic plans of making the man come out of his hiding-place at the point of her pistol; and Virginia could cock a pistol and wasn't covered with cold shivers at the sight of one, as she was. If it had only been Francie, whose shrill voice could have been heard over the side of the earth, or Juliet, whose long legs would have left burglar, and house, too, in the background between the opening and slamming of a door. Either of them was so much more fit than she, the chicken-hearted one of the family, to cope with this creature. And they were all gone to the wedding with Fred, and would not be at home till to-morrow; and Tom had just returned from the town and handed her his roll of bills, and told her to take care of it till he came back from galloping down to the works with Jules; and she had tucked it into her belt, and had asked him, a little quakingly, what if any of the men of the Dead Line that they had heard of or Red Dan or an Apache came along; and he had laughed, and said she had better ask them in and reproach them for making such strangers of themselves as not to have called in the two years she had been in this part of the country; and she had the two maids with her, and he should be back directly. And she had looked out after him a moment over the wide prairie to the hills, all bathed in moonlight, and felt as if she were a spirit alone in a dead world. And here she was now, the two maids away in the little wing, locked out by the main house, alone with a burglar, and not another being nearer than the works, a half-mile off.

How did this man know that she was without any help here? How did he know that Tom was coming back with the money to pay the men that night? How did he happen to be aware that Tom's money was all in the house? Evidently he was one of the men. No one else could have known anything about it. If that money was taken, nobody would believe the story; Tom would be cashiered; he never could live through the disgrace; he would die of a broken heart, and she of another. They had come out to this remote and lonesome country to build up a home and a fortune; and so many people would be stricken with them! What a mischance for her to be left with the whole thing in her hands, her little, weak, trembling hands—Tom's honor, his good name and his success, their fortune, the welfare of the whole family, the livelihood of all the men, the safety of the enterprise! What made Tom risk things so! How could he put her in such jeopardy? To be sure, he thought the dogs would be safeguard enough, but they had gone scouring after him. And if they hadn't, how could dogs help her with a man under the bed?

It was worse than any loss of money to have such a wretch as this so near one, so shudderingly, so awfully near, to be so close as this to the bottomless pit itself! What was she to do? Escape? The possibility did not cross her mind. Not once did she think of letting Tom's money go. All but annihilated by terror in that heartbeat, she herself was the last thing she thought of.

Light and electricity are swift, but thought is swifter. As I said, this was all in the fraction of a second. Then Mrs. Laughton was on her feet again and before a pendulum could have more than swung backward. The man must know she saw him. She took the light brass bedstead and sent it rolling away from her with all her might

and main leaving the creature uncovered. He lay easily
on one side, a stout little club like a policeman's billy in
his hand, some weapons gleaming in his belt, putting up
the other hand to grasp the bedstead as it rolled away.

"You look pretty, don't you?" said she.

Perhaps this was as much of a shock to the man as his
appearance had been to her. He was not acquainted with
the saying that it is only the unexpected that happens.

"Get up," said she. "I'd *be* a man if I *was* a man. Get
up. I'm not going to hurt you."

If the intruder had any sense of humor, this might
have touched it; the idea of this little fairy-queen of a
woman, almost small enough to have stepped out of a
rain-lily, hurting him! But it was so different from what
he had been awaiting that it startled him; and then, perhaps, he had some of the superstition that usually haunts
the evil and ignorant, and felt that such small women
were uncanny. He was on his feet now, towering over
her.

"No," said he, gruffly; "I don't suppose you're going
to hurt me. And I'm not going to hurt you, if you hand
over that money."

"What money?" opening her eyes with a wide sort of
astonishment.

"Come! None of your lip. I want that money!"

"Why, I haven't any money! Oh, yes, I have, to be
sure, but—"

"I thought you'd remember it," said the man, with a
grin.

"But I want it!" she exclaimed.

"I want it, too!" said he.

"Oh, it wouldn't do you any good," she reasoned.
"Fifteen dollars. And it's all the money I've got in the
world!"

"I don't want no fifteen dollars," said the man; "and I don't want none of your chinning. I want the money your husband's going to pay off with—"

"Oh, Tom's money!" in quite a tone of relief. "Oh! I haven't anything to do with Tom's money. If you can get any money out of Tom it's more than *I* can do. And I wouldn't advise you to try, either; for he always carries a pistol in the same pocket with it, and he's covered all over with knives and derringers and bull-dogs, so that sometimes *I* don't like to go near him till he's unloaded. You have to, in this country of desperadoes. You see—"

"Yes, I see, you little hen-sparrer," his eyes coming back to her from a survey of the room, "that you've got Tom's money in the house here, and would like to throw me off the scent!"

"If I had," said she, "you'd only get it across my dead body! Hadn't you better look for it, and have me tell you when you're hot and when you're cold?"

"Come!" said he, again; "I've had enough of your slack—"

"You're not very polite," she said, with something like a pout.

"People in my line ain't," he answered, grimly. "I want that money! and I want it now! I've no time to lose. I'd rather come by it peaceable," he growled, "but if—"

"Well, you can take it; of course, you're the stronger. But I told you before, it's all I have, and I've very particular use for it. You just sit down!" she cried, indicating a chair, with the air of really having been alone so long in these desolate regions as to be glad of having some one to talk to, and throwing herself into the big one opposite, because in truth she could not stand up another moment. And perhaps feeling as if a wren were expostulating with him about robbing her nest, the man dropped the angry arm with which he had threatened her, and leaned over the back of the chair.

"There it is," said she, "right under your hand all the time. You won't have to rip up the mattress for it, or rummage the clothes-press, or hunt through the broken crockery on the top shelves of the kitchen cupboard," she ran on, as if she were delighted to hear the sound of her own voice, and couldn't talk fast enough. "I always leave my purse on the dressing-case, though Tom has told me, time and again, it wasn't safe. But out here—"

"Stop!" thundered the man. "If you know enough to stop. Stop! or I'll cut your cursed tongue out and make you stop. And then, I suppose, you'd gurgle. That's not what I want—though I'll take it. I've told *you*, time and again, that I want the paymaster's money. That isn't right under my hand—and where is it? I'll put daylight through that little false heart of yours if you don't give it to me without five more words—"

"And I've told you just as often that I've nothing to do with the paymaster's money, and I wish you would put daylight *anywhere*, for then my husband would come home and make an end of you!" And with the great limpid tears overflowing her blue eyes, Rose Laughton knew that the face she turned up at him was enough to melt the sternest heart going.

"Do you mean to tell me—" said he, evidently wavering, and possibly inclining to doubt if, after all, she were not telling the truth, as no man in his senses would leave such a sum of money in the keeping of such a simpleton.

"I don't mean to tell you anything!" she cried. "You won't believe a word I say, and I never had any one doubt my word before. I *hate* to have you take that fifteen dollars, though. You never would in the world, if you knew how much self-denial it stands for. Every time I think I would like an ice-cream, out in this wilderness, where you might as well ask for an iceberg, I've made Tom give me the *price* of one. You won't find anything but ribbons *there*. And when I've felt as if I should go wild if I couldn't have a box of Huyler's candy, I've made Tom give me the price of *that*. There's only powder and tweezers and frizzes in those boxes," as he went over the top of the dressing-case, still keeping a lookout on her. "And when we were all out of lager and apollinaris, and Tom couldn't—that's my laces, and I wish you wouldn't finger them; I don't believe your hands are clean—and Tom couldn't get anything to drink, I've made him put in the price of a drink, and lots of ten-cent pieces came that way, and—But I don't imagine you care to hear about all that. What makes you look at me so?" For the man had left his search again, and his glance was piercing her through and through. "Oh, your eyes are like augers turning to live coals!" she cried. "Is that the way you look at your wife? Do you look at your children the same way?"

"That lay won't work," said he, with another grin. "I ain't got no feelings to work on. I ain't got no wife or kids."

"I'm sure that's fortunate," said Mrs. Laughton. "A family wouldn't have any peace of their lives with you following such a dangerous business. And they couldn't see much of you either. I must say I think you'd be a great deal happier if you reformed—I mean—well, if you left this business, and took up a quarter-section, and had a wife and—"

"Look here!" cried the man, his patience gone. "Are you a fool, or are you bluffing me? I've half a mind to knock your head in," he cried, "and hunt the house over for myself! I would, if there was time."

"You wouldn't find anything if you did," she returned, leaning back in her chair. "I've looked often enough, when I thought Tom had some money. I never found any. What are you going to do now?" with a cry of alarm at his movement.

"I'm going to tie you hand and foot first—"

"Oh, I wouldn't! I'd rather you wouldn't—really! I promise you I won't leave this chair—"

"I don't mean you shall."

"Oh, how can you treat me so!" she exclaimed, lifting up her streaming face. "You don't look like a person to treat a woman so. I don't like to be tied; it makes me feel so helpless."

"What kind of a dumb fool be you, anyway?" said the man, stopping a moment to stare at her. And he made a step then toward the high chest of drawers, half bureau, half writing-desk, for a ball of tape he saw lying there.

"Oh!" she cried, remembering the tar-baby. "Don't! Don't go there! For mercy's sake, don't go there!" raising her voice till it was like the wind in the chimney. "Oh, please don't go there!" At which, as if feeling morally, or rather immorally, sure that what he had come for was in that spot, he seized the handles of the drawer, and down fell the lid upon his head with a whack that jammed his hat over his eyes and blinded him with pain and fury for an instant. And in that instant she had whipped the roll of money from her belt, and had dropped it underneath her chair. "I knew it!" she cried. "I knew it would! It always does. I told you not to go."

"You shet your mouth quick!" roared the man, with a splutter of oaths between each word.

"That's right," she said, leaning over the arm of the

chair, her face like a pitying saint's. "Don't mind me, I always tell Tom to swear, when he jams his thumb. I know how it is myself when I'm driving a nail. It's a great relief. I'd put some cold water on your head, but I promised you I wouldn't stir out of the chair—"

The man went and sat down in the chair on whose back he had been leaning.

"I swear, I don't know what to make of you," said he, rubbing his head ruefully.

"You can make friends with me," said she. "That's what you can do. I'm sure I've shown you that I'm friendly enough. I never believe any harm of any one till I see it myself. I don't blame you for wanting the money. I'm always in want of money. I've told you you might take mine, though I don't want you to. But I shouldn't give you Tom's money, even if I knew where it was. Tom would kill me if I did, and I might as well be killed by you as by Tom—and better. You can make friends with me, and be some protection to me till my husband comes. I'm expecting him and Jules every moment."

The man started to his feet.

"Do you see that?" he cried, holding his revolver under her nose. "Look right into that gun! We'll have no more fooling. It'll be your last look if you don't tell me where that money is before I count three."

She put out her hand and calmly moved it aside.

"I've looked into those things ever since I've lived on the prairie," said she. "And I dare say it won't go off— mine won't. Besides, I know very well you wouldn't shoot a woman, and you can't make bricks without straw; and then I've told you I don't know anything about that money."

"You are a game one," said he.

1963

"No, I'm not," she replied. "I'm the most tremendous coward. I've come out here in this wild country to live, and I'm alone a great deal, and I quake at every sound, every creak of a timber, every rustle of the grass. And you don't know anything about what it is to have your heart stand still with horror of a wild beast or a wild Indian or a deserter—a deserting soldier. There's a great Apache down there now, stretched out in his blanket on the floor, before the fire in the kitchen. And I came up here as quick as I could, to lock the door behind us and sit up till Tom came home, and I declare, I never was so thankful in all my life as I was just now to see a white face when I looked at you!"

"Well, I'll be—! Apache!" cried the visitor. "See here, little one, you've saved your husband's money for him. You're a double-handful of pluck. I haven't any idea but you know where it's hid—but I've got to be making tracks. If it wasn't for waking that Apache I'd leave Red Dan's handwriting on the wall."

And almost while he was speaking he had swung himself out of the window to the roof of the porch and had dropped to the ground and made off.

Mrs. Laughton waited till she thought he must be out of hearing, leaning out as if she were gazing at the moon. Then she softly shut and fastened the sash, and crept with shaking limbs to the door and unlocked it, and fell in a dead faint across the threshold. And there, when he returned some three-quarters of an hour later, Tom found her.

"Oh, Tom!" she sobbed, when she became conscious that she was lying in his arms, his heart beating like a trip-hammer, his voice hoarse with fright as he implored her to open her eyes; "*is* there an Apache in the kitchen?"

1964

RUBAIYAT OF MATHIEU LETTELLIER

BY WALLACE BRUCE AMSBARY

Dere's six chil*dren* in our fam'lee,
   Dey's mos'ly girls an' boys;
'Toinette an' me wos t'ankful sure
   For all de happy joys;
Dere's Pierre, an' little Rosalie,
   Antoine, Marie an' Jeanne,
An' Paul he's com' now soon twelf year,
   Mos' close to be a man.

I's lof' all of *la petite femme,*
   De garçon mak' me proud,
I haf' gr'ad aspiratione
   For all dat little crowd;
My Pierre shall be wan doctor mans,
   Rosalie will teach school,
Antoine an' Jeanne shall rone de farm,
   Marie som' man will rule.

An' Paul shall be a *curé* sure,
   I'll haf' heem educate',
I work it all out on my head,
   Oh, I am moch elate;
Dis all of course w'en dey grow op;
   But I t'ink 'bout it now;
So w'en de tam' was com' for ac',
   I'll know de way an' how.

1965

RUBAIYAT OF MATHIEU LETTELLIER

Long tam' ago, w'en Paul firs' com',
  He mak' a lot of noise;
He's keep me trot, bot' day an' night,
  He was wan naughty boys;
At wan o'clock, at two o'clock,
  An*nee* ol' tam' suit heem,
He's mak' us geeve de gran' parade
  Jus' as he tak' de w'im.

Sooding molass' an' peragork,
  On heem ve pour it down,
An' soon he let his music op,
  An' don' ac' more lak' clown,
An' den *ma femme* an' me lay down
  To get a little doze,
For w'en you are wan fam'lee man
  You don' gat moch repose.

But w'at's de use to mak' de kick,
  Dees fellows boss de place;
I'd radder hear de healt'y lung
  An' see de ruddy face
Dan run a gr'ad big doctor's bill,
  An' geeve de ol' sex*tone*
De job, for bury all my kids,
  An' leave me all alone.

'An' so our hands is quite ver' full,
  Will be, for som' tam' long,
But ven old age is dreeft our vay
  An' rest is our belong,
It's den ve'll miss de gran' rac*quette,*—
  May want again de noise
Of six more little children
  An' mos'ly girls and boys.
1966

BIGGS' BAR

BY HOWARD V. SUTHERLAND

'Twas a sultry afternoon, about the middle of July,
And the men who loafed in Dawson were feeling very
dry.
Of liquor there had long been none except a barrel or
two,
And that was kept by Major Walsh for himself and a
lucky few.

Now, the men who loaf in Dawson are loafers to the
bone,
And take it easy in a way peculiarly their own;
They sit upon the sidewalks and smoke and spit and
chew,
And watch the other loafers, and wonder who is who.

They only work in winter, when the days are short and
cold,
And then they heat their cabins, and talk and talk of
gold;
They talk about provisions, and sometimes take a walk,
But then they hurry back again and talk, and talk, and
talk.

And the men who loaf in Dawson are superior to style,
For the man who wears a coat *and* vest is apt to cause a
smile;

While he who sports suspenders or a belt would be a butt,
And cause ironic comment, and end by being cut.

The afternoon was sultry, as I said some time before;
'Twas fully ninety in the shade (in the sun a darn sight
    more),
And the men who sat on the sidewalks were, one and all,
    so dry
That only one perspired, though every one did try.

Six men were sitting in a line and praying God for air;
They were Joaquin Miller and "Lumber" Lynch and
    "Stogey" Jack Ver Mehr,
"Swift-water" Bill and "Caribou" Bill and a sick man
    from the hills,
Who came to town to swap his dust for a box of liver
    pills.

I said they prayed for air, and yet perhaps I tell a lie,
For none of them are holy men, and all of them were
    dry;
And so I guess 'tis best for me to say just what I think—
They prayed the Lord to pity them and send them all a
    drink.

Then up spoke Joaquin Miller, as he shook his golden
    locks,
And picked the Dawson splinters from his moccasins
    and socks
(The others paid attention, for when times are out of
    joint
What Joaquin Miller utters is always to the point):

"A foot-sore, weary traveler," the Poet then began,
"Did tell me many moons ago,—and oh! I loved the
      man,—
That Biggs who owns the claim next mine had started
      up a bar.
Let's wander there and quench our thirst." All an-
      swered, "Right you are."

Now, Biggs is on Bonanza Creek, claim ninety-six, be-
      low;
There may be millions in it, and there may not; none will
      know
Until he gets to bedrock or till bedrock comes to him—
For Arthur takes it easy and is strictly in the swim.

It is true, behind his cabin he has sunk a mighty shaft
(When the husky miners saw it they turned aside and
      laughed) ;
But Biggs enjoys his bacon, and smokes his pipe and
      sings,
Content to be enrolled among the great Bonanza Kings.

'Tis full three miles from Dawson town to Biggs' little
      claim;
The miners' curses on the trail would make you blush
      with shame
The while they slip, or stub their toes against the roots,
      or sink
Twelve inches in the mud and slime before their eyes can
      wink.

But little cared our gallant six for roots, or slime, or
      mud,
For they were out for liquor as a soldier is for blood;

1969

They hustled through the forest, nor stopped until they
    saw
Biggs, wrapt in contemplation, beside his cabin door.

He rose to greet his visitors, and ask them for the news,
And said he was so lonesome that he always had the
    blues;
He hadn't seen a paper for eighteen months, he said,
And that had been in Japanese—a language worse than
    dead.

They satisfied his thirst for news, then thought they of
    their own,
And Miller looked him in the eye and gave a little groan,
And all six men across their mouths did pass a sun-burnt
    hand
In a manner most deliberate, which all can understand.

"We heard you keep a bar, good Biggs," the gentle Poet
    said!
"And so we thought we'd hold you up, and we are almost
    dead!"
He said no more.   Biggs understood, and thusly spoke to
    them
In accents somewhat British and prefixed with a "Hem!"

"The bar you'll find a few yards hence as up that trail
    you go;
I never keep my liquor in the blooming 'ouse, you know.
Just mush along and take a drink, and when you are
    content
Come back and tell me, if you can, who now is Presi-
    dent."

They mushed along, those weary men, nor looked to left
    or right,
But thought of how each cooling drink would trickle out
    of sight;
And very soon they found the goal they came for from
    afar—
A keg, half full of water, in a good old gravel bar!

THE BACKSLIDING BROTHER

BY FRANK L. STANTON

De screech owl screech f'um de ol' barn lof';
"You drinked yo' dram sence you done swear off;
       En you gwine de way
       Whar' de sinners stay,
En Satan gwine ter roas' you at de Jedgmint Day!"

Den de ol' ha'nt say, f'um de ol' chu'ch wall:
"You des so triflin' dat you *had* ter fall!
       En you gwine de way
       Whar' de brimstone stay,
En Satan gwine ter roas' you at de Jedgmint Day!"

Den I shake en shiver,
En I hunt fer kiver,
En I cry ter de good Lawd, "Please deliver!"
       I tell 'im plain
       Dat my hopes is vain,
En I drinked my dram fer ter ease my pain!

Den de screech owl screech f'um de north ter south
"You drinked yo' dram, en you *smacked* yo' *mouth!*
       En you gwine de way
       Whar' de brimstone stay,
En Satan gwine ter roas' you at de Jedgmint Day!"

YE LEGEND OF SIR YRONCLADDE

BY WILBUR D. NESBIT

Now, whenne ye goode knyghte Yroncladde
　　Hadde dwelte in Paradyse
A matter of a thousand yeares,
　　He syghed some grievous syghes,
And went unto the entrance gate
　　To speake hym in thys wyse:

"Beholde, I do not wysh to make
　　A rackette, nor a fuss,
And yet I fayne wolde hie awaye
　　And cease from livyng thus;
For it is moste too peaceful here,
　　And sore monotonous."

"Oh, verie welle," ye keeper sayde,
　　"You shall have your desyre:
Go downe uponne ye earth agayne
　　To see whatte you admyre—
But take goode heede that you shall keepe
　　Your trolley on ye wyre."

Ryghte gladde was goode Sir Yroncladde
　　To see ye gates unsealed.
He toke a jumpe strayghte through ye cloudes
　　To what was there revealed,
And strayghtwaye lit uponne ye grounde
　　Whych was a footeball field!

1973

"Gadzookes!" he sayde; "now, here is sporte!
   Thys is a goodlie syghte.
For joustynges soche as here abound
   I have an appetyte;
So I will amble to ye scrappe,
   For that is my delyghte."

He strode into ye hurtlynge mass,
   Whence rose a thrillynge sounde
Of class yelles, sygnalles, breakynge bones,
   And moanynges all arounde;
And thenne ye footeballe menne tooke hym
   And pushed hym in ye grounde!

They brake hys breastplayte into bits,
   And shattered all hys greaves;
They fractured bothe hys myghtie armes
   Withynne hys chaynemayle sleeves,
And wounde hys massyve legges ynto
   Some oryentalle weaves.

Uppe rose ye brave Sir Yroncladde
   And groaned, "I hadde no wrong!
I'll hustle back to Paradyse,
   And ryng ye entraunce gong;
For thys new croppe of earthlie knyghtes
   At joustynge is too strong;
And henceforth thys is my resolve:
   To staye where I belong!"

1974

WINTER DUSK

BY R. K. MUNKITTRICK

The prospect is bare and white,
    And the air is crisp and chill;
While the ebon wings of night
    Are spread on the distant hill.

The roar of the stormy sea
    Seem the dirges shrill and sharp
That winter plays on the tree—
    His wild Æolian harp.

In the pool that darkly creeps
    In ripples before the gale,
A star like a lily sleeps
    And wiggles its silver tail.

A MOTHER OF FOUR

BY JULIET WILBOR TOMPKINS

"You are fortunate to find us alone, Mrs. Merritt. With four girls, it is simply terrible—callers underfoot wherever you stir. You must know something about it, with two daughters; so you can fancy it multiplied by two. Really, sometimes I get out of all patience—I haven't a corner of my house to myself on Sundays! But I realize it is the penalty for having four lively daughters, and I have to put up with it."

Mrs. Merritt, the visitor, had a gently worried air as she glanced from the twins, thin and big-boned, reading by the fire, to pretty, affected Amélie at the tea-table, and the apathetic Enid furtively watching the front steps from the bay window. Something in her expression seemed to imply a humble wonder as to what might constitute the elements of high popularity, since her two dear girls—

"Of course, mine have their friends," she asserted; it was an admission that perhaps the door-bell was not overworked. "I enjoy young life," she added.

"Oh, yes, in moderation!" Mrs. Baldwin laughed from the depths of the complacent prosperity that irradiated her handsome white hair and active brown eyes, her pleasant rosiness, and even her compact stoutness, suggesting strength rather than weight. "But since Enid became engaged, that means Harry all the time—there's my library gone; and with the other three filling both drawing-rooms

1976

and the reception-room, I have to take to the dining-room, myself! There they begin," she added, as Enid left the window and slipped out into the hall, closing the door after her. "Now we shall have no peace until Monday morning. You know how it is!"

Mrs. Merritt seemed depressed, and soon took her leave.

The twins, when they were left alone in the drawing-room, lifted their heads and exchanged long and solemn looks; then returned to their reading in silence. When it grew too dark by the fire, they carried their books to the bay window, but drew back as they saw a pale and puny youth with a retreating chin coming up the front steps.

"The rush has begun," murmured Cora.

"Amélie can have him," Dora returned. "Let's fly."

They retreated up-stairs and read peacefully until tea-time. The bell did not ring again. When they came down, Mrs. Baldwin eyed them irritably.

"Why don't you ask the Carryl boys in to Sunday tea some time? They will think you have forgotten them. And Mr. White and that nice Mr. Morton who lives with him—I am afraid you have offended them in some way. They used to be here all the time."

"They only came twice, and those were party calls," said Dora bluntly.

"My dear, you have forgotten," was the firm answer. "They were here constantly. I shall send them a line; I don't like to have them think we have gone back on them."

"Oh, I—I wouldn't," began Cora, but was put down with decision:

"When I need your advice, Cora, I will ask for it. Amélie, dear, you look tired; I am afraid you have had too much gaiety this afternoon."

"Oh, I love it! It's the breath of life to me," said

Amélie rapturously. The twins again exchanged solemn looks and sat down to their tea in silence. Mrs. Baldwin attacked them peevishly at intervals; she was cross at Enid also, who had not kept Harry to supper, and preserved an indifferent silence under questioning. "When I was your age—!" was the burden of her speech.

"I must give a dance for you young people," she decided. "You need livening up."

"Oh, lovely!" exclaimed Amélie.

"We have not had one this winter—I don't know what I have been thinking about," Mrs. Baldwin went on with returning cheerfulness. "We won't ask more than a hundred. You must have a new frock, Amélie. Enid, how is your blue one?"

"Oh, all right," said Enid indifferently. Mrs. Baldwin turned to the twins, and found them looking frankly dismayed.

"Well, what is it now?" she exclaimed. "I am sure I try to give you as good times as any girls in town; not many mothers on my income would do half so much. And you sit looking as if you were going to execution!"

"We—we do appreciate it, mother," urged Cora, unhappily.

"But we aren't howling successes at parties," Dora added.

"Nonsense! You have partners to spare." Mrs. Baldwin was plainly angry. "No child of mine was ever a wallflower, nor ever will be. Never let me hear you say such a thing again. You would have twice the attention if you weren't always poking off by yourselves; and as it is, you have more than most girls. You frighten the men —they think you are proud. Show a little interest in them and see how pleased they will be!"

The twins looked dubious, and seized the first chance

to escape. In their own room they confronted each other dismally.

"Of course they will ask us, in our own house; we won't have to sit and sit," said Cora with a sigh.

"But it's almost worse when they ask you for that reason," objected Dora.

"I know! I feel so sorry for them, and so apologetic. If mother would *only* let us go and teach at Miss Browne's; then we could show we were really good for something. We shouldn't have to shine at parties."

"We shouldn't have to go to them! Come on, let's do some Latin. I want to forget the hateful thing."

Cora got down the books and drew their chairs up to the student-lamp. "I know I shouldn't be such a stick if I didn't have to wear low neck," she said. "I am always thinking about those awful collar-bones, and trying to hold my shoulders so as not to make them worse."

"Oh, don't I know!" Dora had slipped on a soft red wrapper, and threw a blue one to her sister. When they were curled up in their big, cushioned chairs, they smiled appreciatively at each other.

"Isn't this nicer than any party ever invented?" they exclaimed. Dora opened her books with energy, but Cora sat musing.

"I dare say that somewhere there are parties for our kind," she said, finally. "Not with silly little chinless boys or popular men who are always trying to get away, but men who study and care about things—who go to Greece and dig ruins, for instance, or study sociology, and think more about one's mind than one's collar-bones."

Dora shook her head. "But they don't go to parties!"

"Both Mr. Morton and Mr. White do, sometimes," Cora suggested. "They aren't like the rest. I thought that tenement-house work they told us about was most interesting. But they would call if they wanted to," she added.

The twins in wrappers, bending over their books, had a certain comeliness. There was even an austere beauty in their wide, high foreheads, their fine, straight dark hair, their serious gray eyes and sensitive mouths, pensive but not without humor and sweetness. But the twins in evening dress, their unwilling hair flower-crowned and bolstered into pompadours, their big-boned thinness contrasted with Amélie's plump curves, their elbows betraying the red disks of serious application, were quite another matter, and they knew it. The night of the dance they came down-stairs with solemn, dutiful faces, and lifted submissive eyes to their mother for judgment. She was looking charmingly pretty herself, carrying her thick white hair with a humorous boldness, and her smiling brown eyes were younger than their gray ones.

"Very well, twinnies! Now you look something like human girls," she said gaily. "Run and have a beautiful time. Ah, Amélie, you little fairy! They will all be on their knees to you to-night. Where is Enid?"

"Nowhere near dressed, and she won't hurry," Amélie explained. "Oh, I am so excited, I shall die! What if no one asks me to dance!"

"Silly!" Mrs. Baldwin laughed. "I am only afraid of your dancing yourself to death. Ah, Mrs. Merritt, how good of you to come with your dear girls! And Mr. Merritt—this is better than I dared hope."

The rooms filled rapidly. Enid, after one languid waltz, disappeared with Harry and was not seen again till supper. Amélie flew from partner to partner, pouring streams of vivacious talk into patient masculine ears. The twins were dutifully taken out in turn and unfailingly brought back. Both Mr. White and Mr. Morton came, serious young men who danced little, and looked on more as if the affair were a problem in sociology than an enter-tainment. There were plenty of men, for Mrs. Baldwin's entertainments had a reputation in the matter of supper, music, and floors.

"After you've worked through the family, you can have a ripping old time," Cora heard one youth explain to another; a moment later he stood in front of her, beg-ging the honor of a waltz. She felt no resentment; her sympathies were all with him. She looked up with gentle seriousness.

"You needn't, you know," she said. "Dora and I don't really expect it—we understand." He looked so puzzled that she added: "I overheard you just now, about 'work-ing through the family.'"

He grew distressfully red and stammered wildly. Cora came at once to his rescue.

"Really, it's all right. We don't like parties, ourselves; only it is hard on mother to have such sticks of daughters, so we do our best. But we never mind when people don't ask us. Sometimes we almost wish they wouldn't."

The youth was trying desperately to collect himself. "What *do* you like, then?" he managed to ask.

"Oh, books, and the country, and not having to be in-troduced to people." She was trying to put him at his ease. "We really do like dancing: we do it better than you'd think, for mother made us keep at it. If only we didn't have to have partners and think of things to say to them!" She held out her hand. "Thank you ever so much for ask-ing me, but I'd truly rather not." He wrung her hand, muttered something about "later, then," and fled, still red about the ears. Cora returned to her mother.

"Well, my dear, you seemed to be having a tremendous flirtation with that youth," laughed Mrs. Baldwin. "Such

a hand-clasp at parting! Don't dance too hard, child."
She turned to the half-dozen parents supporting her.
"These crazy girls of mine will dance themselves to death
if I don't keep an eye on them," she explained. "Amélie
says, 'Mother, how can I help splitting my dances, when
they beg me to?' I am always relieved when the dance is
over and they are safe in bed—then I know they aren't
killing themselves. The men have no mercy—they never
let them rest an instant."

"I don't see Miss Enid about," suggested Mr. Merritt.
"I suppose she and her Harry—!"

"Oh, I suppose so!" Mrs. Baldwin shook her head resignedly. "The bad child insists on being married in the
spring, but I simply can not face the idea. What can I
do to prevent it, Mrs. Merritt?"

"I am afraid you can't," smiled Mrs. Merritt. "We
mothers all have to face that."

"Ah, but not so soon! It is dreadful to have one's girls
taken away. I watch the others like a hawk; the instant
a man looks too serious—pouf!—I whisk him away!"

Cora stood looking down, with set lips; a flush had
risen in her usually pale cheeks. Dora, setting free an im-
patient partner, joined her and they drew aside.

"It does make me so ashamed!" said Cora, impul-
sively.

"I think mother really makes herself believe it," said
Dora, with instant understanding.

They watched Amélie flutter up to their mother to have
a bow retied, and stand radiant under the raillery, though
she made a decent pretense of pouting. Her partner vanished, and Mrs. Baldwin insisted on her resting "for one
minute," which ended when another partner appeared.

"Amélie is asked much more than we are, always,"
Cora suggested. Dora nodded at the implication.

"I know. I wonder why it never seems quite real. Perhaps because the devoted ones are such silly little men."

"Or seem to us so," Cora amended conscientiously. "Don't you wish we might creep up-stairs? Oh, me, here comes a man, just hating it! Which do you suppose he will—Oh, thank you, with pleasure, Mr. Dorr!" Cora was led away, and Dora slipped into the next room, that her mother might not be vexed at her partnerless state.

Mrs. Baldwin saw to it that the twins had partners for supper, and seated them at a table with half a dozen lively spirits, where they ate in submissive silence while the talk flowed over and about them. No one seemed to remember that they were there, yet they felt big and awkward, conspicuous with neglect, thoroughly forlorn. When they rose, the others moved off in a group, leaving them stranded. Mrs. Baldwin beckoned them to her table with her fan.

"Well, twinnies, yours was the noisiest table in the room," she laughed. "I was quite ashamed of you! When these quiet girls get going—!" she added expressively to her group. The twins flushed, standing with shamed eyes averted. In the rooms above the music had started, and the bright procession moved up the stairs with laughter and the shine of lights on white shoulders; they all seemed to belong together, to be glad of one another. "Well, run along and dance your little feet off," said Mrs. Baldwin gaily.

They hurried away, and without a word mounted by the back stairs to their own room. When their eyes met, a flash of anger kindled, grew to a blaze.

"Oh, I won't stand it, I won't!" exclaimed Dora, jerking the wreath of forget-me-nots out of her hair and throwing it on the dressing-table. "We have been humiliated long enough. Cora, we're twenty-four; it is time we had our own way."

Cora was breathing hard. "Dora, I will never go to another party as long as I live," she said.

"Nor I," declared Dora.

They sat down side by side on the couch to discuss ways and means. A weight seemed to be lifted off their lives. In the midst of their eager planning the door opened and Mrs. Baldwin looked in at them with a displeased frown.

"Girls, what does this mean?" she exclaimed. "Come down at once. What are you thinking of, to leave your guests like this!"

The twins felt that the moment had come, and instinctively clasped hands as they rose to meet it.

"Mother," said Dora firmly, "we have done with parties forever and ever. No one likes us nor wants to dance with us, and we can't stand it any more."

"Miss Browne still wants us to come there and teach," Cora added, her voice husky but her eyes bright. "So we can be self-supporting, if—if you don't approve. We are twenty-four, and we have to live our own lives."

They stood bravely for annihilation. Mrs. Baldwin laughed.

"You foolish twinnies! I know—some one has been hurting your feelings. Believe me, my dears, even I did not always get just the partner my heart was set on! And I cried over it in secret, just like any other little girl. That is life, you know—we can't give up before it. Now smooth yourselves and come down, for some of them are leaving."

She blew them a kiss and went off smiling. After a dejected silence Dora took up the forget-me-not wreath and replaced it.

"I suppose we might as well finish out this evening," she said. "But the revolution has begun, Cora!"

"The revolution has begun," Cora echoed.

In the drawing-room they found Mrs. Baldwin talking with Mr. Morton and Mr. White. They were evidently trying to say good night, but she was holding them as inexorably as if she had laid hands on their coats; or so it seemed to the troubled twins. She summoned her daughters with her bright, amused glance.

"My dears," she said, "these two good friends were going to run away just because they do not dance the cotillion. We can't allow that. Suppose you take them to the library and make them wholly comfortable. Indeed, they have danced enough, Mr. White; I am thankful to have them stop. I will take the blame if their partners are angry."

She nodded a smiling dismissal. Disconcerted, wholly ill at ease, the four went obediently to the library, deserted now that the cotillion was beginning. The two men struggled valiantly with the conversation, but the twins sat stricken to shamed dumbness: no topic could thrive in the face of their mute rigidity. Silences stalked the failing efforts. Mr. White's eyes clung to the clock while his throat dilated with secret yawns; Mr. Morton twisted restlessly and finally let a nervous sigh escape. Dora suddenly clasped her hands tightly together.

"We hate it just as much as you do," she said distinctly.

They turned startled faces toward her. Cora paled, but flew to her sister's aid.

"We knew you didn't want to come," she added with tremulous frankness. "We would have let you off if we could. If you want to go now, we won't be—hurt."

They rose, and so did the bewildered visitors.

"I am afraid you have—misunderstood," began Mr. White.

"No; we have always understood—everybody," said Dora, "but we pretended not to, because mother— But now we have done with society. It is a revolution, and this is our last party. Good night." She held out her hand.

"Good night," repeated Cora, offering hers. The guests took them with the air of culprits; relief was evidently drowned in astonishment.

"Well, good night—if we must," they said awkwardly.

Mrs. Baldwin, looking into the library half an hour later, found the twins sitting there alone.

"Where are your cavaliers?" she demanded.

"They left long ago," Dora explained sleepily. "Mayn't we go to bed?"

"Oh, for pity's sake—go!" was the exasperated answer.

In the morning the twins appeared braced for revolution. When a reception for that afternoon was mentioned, they announced firmly that they were not going.

"I think you are wise," said Mrs. Baldwin amiably. "You both look tired."

They were conscious of disappointment as well as relief; it was the establishment of a principle they wanted, not coddling. Three weeks went by in the same debilitating peace. The twins were smiled on and left wholly free. They had almost come to believe in a bloodless victory, when Mrs. Baldwin struck—a masterly attack where they were weakest. Her weapon was—not welcome temper, but restrained pathos.

"A mere fourteen at dinner and a few coming in to

dance afterward, and I do want you twinnies to be there. Now I have not asked one thing of you for three weeks; don't you think you owe Mother some little return?"

"But—!" began the twins, with a rush of the well-known arguments. Mrs. Baldwin would not combat.

"I ask it as a favor, dear girls," she said gently. They clung to their refusal, but were obviously weakening when she rose to her climax: "Mr. White and Mr. Morton have accepted!" She left them with that, confident and humming to herself.

The twins stared at each other in open misery. Reappear now, after the solemn declaration they had made to those two! Their cheeks burned at the thought. They mounted to their room to formulate their resistance, and found two exquisite new gowns, suitable for fairy princesses, spread out like snares. "To please Mother" seemed to be written on every artful fold. And Mrs. Baldwin was not a rich woman, for her way of life; such gowns meant self-denial somewhere. The twins had tears in their eyes.

"But if we give in now, we're lost!" they cried.

Nothing more was said about the dinner, Mrs. Baldwin gaily assuming success, but avoiding the topic. The twins wore a depressed and furtive air. On the fatal day they had a long interview with Miss Browne, of the Browne School, and came away solemn with excitement, to shut themselves in their room for the rest of the afternoon.

A few minutes before the dinner-hour Mrs. Baldwin, triumphant in satin and lace, paused at their door.

"Ready, twinnies?" she began, then stared as though disbelieving her eyes. In the glow of the student-lamp sat the twins, books in their hands and piled high on the table beside them; their smooth, dark hair was unpompadoured, their shoulders were lost in the dark blouses of every day.

"What does this mean?" Mrs. Baldwin asked shortly, fire in her eyes.

"Mother, we told you we could not go to any more parties, and why," Cora answered, a note of pleading in her voice.

"We begin teaching on Monday in Miss Browne's school," added Dora more stoutly. "We have tried your way for years and years, mother. Now we have to try ours."

Mrs. Baldwin's lace bertha rose and fell sharply.

"Indeed. I am sorry to disappoint you, but so long as you live under my roof, you will have to conform to the ways of my household."

"Then, mother, we can not stay under your roof."

"As you please! I leave the choice entirely to you." She swept out, leaving them breathless but resolute.

"I am glad of it!" said Dora with trembling lips.

In explaining their absence at dinner, Mrs. Baldwin was lightly humorous about the twins' devotion: one could not weather a headache without the other. Mr. White and Mr. Morton exchanged glances, and showed interest in the topic, as if they were on the track of some new sociological fact.

Later in the evening, the twins, their spirits restored, stole to the top of the stairs and peered down at the whirling couples, exultant not to be among them. Mr. White was standing just below, and he glanced up, as if he might have been listening. His face brightened.

"May I come up?" he signaled, and mounted two steps at a time, keen interest in his thin, intellectual face.

"Is it really headache, or is it revolution?" he asked

without preface. "Morton and I have been longing to know, all the evening."

"Revolution," said the twins.

"How very interesting! Do you know, we came to-night just to see if you would be there. You—you staggered us, the other evening. We were glad when you didn't appear—if you won't misunderstand. It is so unexpected, in this environment. I shall be curious to see how far you can carry it out." He was leaning against the banister, looking at them as if they were abstract propositions rather than young girls, and they felt unwontedly at ease.

"To the very end," Dora asserted. "We begin teaching Monday, and—and we have to find a place to board." Her color rose a little, but she smiled.

"That *is* plucky," he commented. "We can help you there; I know a number of places. When do you want to move?"

"To-morrow," they answered in unison.

He consulted an engagement-book, reflected a few moments, then made a note.

"Morton or I will call for you to-morrow at three," he announced with business-like brevity. "I think I know just the place, but we will give you a choice. If you really wish to move in at once, you could have your things packed, ready to be sent for."

"Oh, we do!" said Cora. He glanced meditatively at their fine and glowing faces.

"Of course you won't be comfortable, luxurious, as you are here," he warned them, with a nod toward the great paneled hall. Mrs. Baldwin passed the drawing-room door below with the stately tread of a reviewing officer.

"Oh, we don't care!" they exclaimed eagerly.

The next day their mother treated the twins as if they were not. She spoke no word to them and did not seem to hear their husky little efforts at reconciliation. They found it hard to remember persistently that they were revolutionists rather than children in disgrace. She was unapproachable in her own room when Mr. White and Mr. Morton came for them.

"Well, we can't help it," they said sadly as they locked their two trunks and went down the stairs.

Three hours later the twins had entered a new world and were rapturously making an omelet in a kitchen that had begun life as a closet, while Mr. Morton put up shelves and hooks and Mr. White tacked green burlap over gloomy wall-paper. Groceries and kitchen utensils and amusing make-shift furniture kept arriving in exciting profusion. They had not dreamed that there was such happiness in the world.

"If only mother will forgive us, it will be simply perfect!" they told each other when they settled down for the night in their hard little cots. They said that many times in the days that followed. The utter joy of work and freedom and simplicity had no other blemish.

For five weeks Mrs. Baldwin remained obdurate. Then, one Sunday afternoon, she appeared, cold, critical, resentful still; lifted her eyebrows at the devices of their light housekeeping; looked disgusted when they pointed out from the window the little café where they sometimes dined; and offered to consent to their social retirement if they would give up the teaching and come home. The twins were troubled and apologetic, but inflexible. They had found the life they were meant for; they could not give it up. If she knew how happy they were!

"How, with your bringing up, you can enjoy this!" she marveled. "It isn't respectable—eating in nasty little holes alone at night!"

"But it is a nice, clean place, and Mr. White and Mr. Morton are nearly always with us," Dora began, then broke off at an expression of pleased enlightenment that flashed across her mother's face. "They are just very good friends," she explained gravely; "they don't take us as girls at all—that is why we have such nice times with them. We are simply comrades, and interested in the same books and problems."

"And they bother about us chiefly because we are a sort of sociological demonstration to them," Cora added. "They like experiments of every kind."

"Ah, yes, I understand," assented Mrs. Baldwin. "Well, you certainly are fixed up very nicely here. If you want anything from home, let me know. After all, it is a piquant little adventure. If you are happy in it, I suppose I ought not to complain."

She was all complacence and compliment the rest of her visit. When she went away, the girls glanced uneasily at each other.

"She took a wrong idea in her head," said Dora. "I do hope we undeceived her. It would be hard for her to understand how wholly mental and impersonal our friendship is with those two."

"Well, she will see in time, when nothing comes of it," said Cora confidently. "That's their ring, now. Oh, Dora, isn't our life nice!"

Mrs. Baldwin, passing down the shabby front steps, might have seen the two men approaching, one with an armful of books and the other with a potted plant; but she apparently did not recognize them, for she stepped into her carriage without a sign. The visit seemed to have left a pleasant memory with her, however; her bland serenity, as she drove away, was not unlike that of the cat which has just swallowed the canary.

FALL STYLES IN FACES*

BY WALLACE IRWIN

Faces this Fall will lead the styles
   More than in former years
With something very neat in smiles
   Well trimmed with eyes and ears.
The Gayer Set, so rumor hints,
   Will have their noses made
In all the famous Highball Tints—
   A bright carnation shade.

For morning wear in club and lobby,
The Dark Brown Taste will be the hobby.

In Wall Street they will wear a gaze
   To match the paving-stones.
(This kind, Miss Ida Tarbell says,
   John Rockefeller owns.)
Loud mouths, sharp glances, furtive looks
   Will be displayed upon
The faces of the best-groomed crooks
   Convened in Washington.

Among the Saints of doubtful morals
Some will wear halos, others laurels.

* From "At the Sign of the Dollar," by Wallace Irwin.   Copyright,
1905, by Fox, Duffield & Co.

Checkered careers will be displayed
   On faces neatly lined,
And vanity will still parade
   In smirks—the cheaper kind.
Chins will appear in Utah's zone
   Adorned with lace-like frizzes,
And something striking will be shown
   In union-labor phizzes.

The gentry who have done the races
Show something new in Poker Faces.

Cheek will supplant Stiff Upper Lips
   And take the place of Chin;
The waiters will wear ostrich tips
   When tipping days begin.
The Wilhelm Moustache, curled with scorn,
   Will show the jaw beneath,
And the Roosevelt Smile will still be worn
   Cut wide around the teeth.

If Frenzied Finance waxes stronger
Stocks will be "short" and faces longer.

But if you have a well-made face
   That's durable and firm,
Its features you need not replace—
   'Twill wear another term.
Two eyes, a nose, a pair of ears,
   A chin that's clean and strong
Will serve their owner many years
   And never go far wrong.

But if your face is shoddy, Brother,
Run to the store and buy another!

HAD A SET OF DOUBLE TEETH

BY HOLMAN F. DAY

Oh, listen while I tell you a truthful little tale
    Of a man whose teeth were double all the solid way
        around;
He could jest as slick as preachin' bite in two a shingle-
        nail,
    Or squonch a molded bullet, sah, and ev'ry tooth was
        sound.

I've seen him lift a keg of pork, a-bitin' on the chine,
    And he 'd clench a rope and hang there like a puppy to
        a root;
And a feller he could pull and twitch and yank up on the
        line,
    But he could n't do no business with that double-toothed
        galoot.

He was luggin' up some shingles,—bunch, sah, under-
        neath each arm,—
    The time that he was shinglin' of the Baptist meetin'-
        house;
The ladder cracked and buckled, but he did n't think no
        harm,
    When all at once she busted, and he started down
        kersouse.

1994

His head, sah, when she busted, it was jest abreast the
    eaves;
  And he nipped, sah, quicker 'n lightnin', and he gripped
    there with his teeth,
And he never dropped the shingles, but he hung to both
    the sheaves,
  Though the solid ground was suttenly more 'n thirty
    feet beneath.

He held there and he kicked there and he squirmed, but
    no one come;
  He was workin' on the roof alone—there war'n't no
    folks around—
He hung like death to niggers till his jaw was set and
    numb,
  And he reely thought he 'd have to drop them shingles
    on the ground.

But all at once old Skillins come a-toddlin' down the
    street;
  Old Skil is sort of hump-backed, and he allus looks
    straight down;
So he never seed the motions of them number 'leven feet,
  And he went a-amblin' by him—the goramded blind old
    clown!

Now this ere part is truthful—ain't a-stretchin' it a
    mite,—
  When the feller seed that Skillins was a-walkin' past
    the place,
Let go his teeth and hollered, but he grabbed back quick
    and tight,
  'Fore he had a chance to tumble, and he hung there by
    the face.

'And he never dropped the shingles, and he never missed
    his grip,
  And he stepped out on the ladder when they raised it
    underneath;
'And up he went a-flukin' with them shingles on his hip,
  And there's the satisfaction of a havin' double teeth.

PLAIN LANGUAGE FROM TRUTHFUL JAMES

BY BRET HARTE

Which I wish to remark—
   And my language is plain —
That for ways that are dark,
   And for tricks that are vain,
The heathen Chinee is peculiar,
   Which the same I would rise to explain.

Ah Sin was his name,
   And I shall not deny
In regard to the same
   What that name might imply;
But his smile it was pensive and childlike,
   As I frequent remarked to Bill Nye.

It was August the third,
   And quite soft was the skies;
Which it might be inferred
   That Ah Sin was likewise;
Yet he played it that day upon William
   And me in a way I despise.

Which we had a small game,
   And Ah Sin took a hand;
It was euchre—the same
   He did not understand;
But he smiled as he sat at the table
   With the smile that was childlike and bland.

LANGUAGE FROM TRUTHFUL JAMES

Yet the cards they were stocked
  In a way that I grieve,
And my feelings were shocked
  At the state of Nye's sleeve,
Which was stuffed full of aces and bowers,
  And the same with intent to deceive.

But the hands that were played
  By that heathen Chinee,
And the points that he made
  Were quite frightful to see,
Till at last he put down a right bower,
  Which the same Nye had dealt unto me.

Then I looked up at Nye,
  And he gazed upon me;
And he rose with a sigh,
  And said, "Can this be?
We are ruined by Chinese cheap labor;"
  And he went for that heathen Chinee.

In the scene that ensued
  I did not take a hand,
But the floor it was strewed
  Like the leaves on the strand
With the cards that Ah Sin had been hiding
  In the game "he did not understand."

In his sleeves, which were long,
  He had twenty-four packs,
Which was coming it strong,
  Yet I state but the facts;
And we found on his nails, which were taper,
  What is frequent in tapers—that's wax.

BRET HARTE

Which is why I remark—
   And my language is plain—
That for ways that are dark,
   And for tricks that are vain,
The heathen Chinee is peculiar,
   Which the same I am free to maintain.

POSSESSION

BY WILLIAM J. LAMPTON

Oh, give me whatever I do not possess,
   No matter whatever it be;
So long as I haven't it that is enough,
   I fancy, to satisfy me.

No matter whatever I happen to have,
   I have it; and what I have not
Seems all that is good of the good things of earth
   To lighten the lack of my lot.

No covetous spirit incites the desire
   To have what I haven't, I'm sure;
Because when I have what I haven't, I want
   What I haven't, the same as before.

So, give me whatever I do not possess,
   No matter whatever it be;
       And yet—
To have what I haven't is having, and that
   Destroys all the pleasure for me.

HER BROTHER: ENFANT TERRIBLE*

BY EDWIN L. SABIN

This is Her brother; angel-faced,—
   Barring freckles and turned-up nose,—
Demon-minded—a word well based,
   As nearer acquaintance will disclose.
From outward guise the most sage of men
   Would never guess what within lies hid!
If years we reckon, in age scant ten;
   If cunning, old as a pyramid.

This is Her brother, who sticks and sticks
   Tighter than even a brother should;
Brimming over with teasing tricks,
   Hardened to bribe and *"please* be good";
And who, when at last afar we deem,
   In some sly recess but lurks in wait
To note the progress of love's young dream—
   And we learn of his presence too late, too late!

This is Her brother, with watchful eyes,
   Piercing, shameless, and indiscreet,
With ears wide open for soft replies
   And sounds that are sibilant and sweet!
With light approach (not a lynx so still),
   With figure meanly invisible,
With threatening voice and iron will,
   And shrill demands or he'll "go and tell!"

*Lippincott's Magazine.

HER BROTHER: ENFANT TERRIBLE

This is Her brother—and I submit
    To paying out quarters and sundry dimes;
This is Her brother—whose urchin wit
    Moves me to wrath a thousand times;
This is Her brother—and hence I smile
    And jest and cringe at his tyranny,
And call him "smart"! But just wait a while
    Till he's *my* brother—and then we'll see!

THE JACKPOT

BY IRONQUILL

I sauntered down through Europe,
   I wandered up the Nile,
I sought the mausoleums where the mummied Pharaohs
      lay;
I found the sculptured tunnel
   Where quietly in style
Imperial sarcophagi concealed the royal clay.
Above the vault was graven deep the motto of the crown:
"Who openeth a jackpot may not always rake it down."

It's strange what deep impressions
   Are made by little things.
Within the granite tunneling I saw a dingy cleft;
It was a cryptic chamber.
   I drew, and got four kings.
But on a brief comparison I laid them down and left,
Because upon the granite stood that sentence bold and
      brown:
"Who openeth a jackpot may not always rake it down."

I make this observation:
   A man with such a hand
Has psychologic feelings that perhaps he should not feel,
But I was somewhat rattled
   And in a foreign land,

And had some dim suspicions, as I had not watched the
    deal.
And there was that inscription, too, in words that seemed
    to frown:
"Who openeth a jackpot may not always rake it down."

These letters were not graven
    In Anglo-Saxon tongue;
Perhaps if you had seen them you had idly passed them
    by.
I studied erudition
    When I was somewhat young;
I recognized the language when it struck my classic eye;
I saw a maxim suitable for monarch or for clown:
"Who openeth a jackpot may not always rake it down."

Detesting metaphysics,
    I can not help but put
A philosophic moral where I think it ought to hang;
I've seen a "boom" for office
    Grow feeble at the root,
Then change into a boomlet—then to a boomerang.
In caucus or convention, in village or in town:
"Who openeth a jackpot may not always rake it down."

DUM VIVIMUS VIGILAMUS

Turn out more ale, turn up the light;
I will not go to bed to-night.
Of all the foes that man should dread
The first and worst one is a bed.
Friends I have had both old and young,
And ale we drank and songs we sung:
Enough you know when this is said,
That, one and all,—they died in bed.
In bed they died and I'll not go
Where all my friends have perished so.
Go you who glad would buried be,
But not to-night a bed for me.

For me to-night no bed prepare,
But set me out my oaken chair.
And bid no other guests beside
The ghosts that shall around me glide;
In curling smoke-wreaths I shall see
A fair and gentle company.
Though silent all, rare revelers they,
Who leave you not till break of day.
Go you who would not daylight see,
But not to-night a bed for me:
For I've been born and I've been wed—
All of man's peril comes of bed.

2005

DUM VIVIMUS VIGILAMUS

And I'll not seek—whate'er befall—
Him who unbidden comes to all.
A grewsome guest, a lean-jawed wight—
God send he do not come to-night!
But if he do, to claim his own,
He shall not find me lying prone;
But blithely, bravely, sitting up,
And raising high the stirrup-cup.
 Then if you find a pipe unfilled,
 An empty chair, the brown ale spilled;
 Well may you know, though naught be said,
 That I've been borne away to bed.

AT AUNTY'S HOUSE

BY JAMES WHITCOMB RILEY

One time, when we'z at Aunty's house—
   'Way in the country!—where
They's ist but woods—an' pigs, an' cows—
   An' all's out-doors an' air!—
An' orchurd-swing; an' churry-trees—
An' *churries* in 'em!—Yes, an' these-
Here red-head birds steals all they please,
   An' tetch 'em ef you dare!—
W'y, wunst, one time, when we wuz there,
   We et out on the porch!

Wite where the cellar-door wuz shut
   The table wuz; an' I
Let Aunty set by me an' cut
   My vittuls up—an' pie.
'Tuz awful funny!—I could see
The red-heads in the churry-tree;
An' bee-hives, where you got to be
   So keerful, goin' by;—
An' "Comp'ny" there an' all!—an' we—
   We et out on the porch!

An' I ist et *p'surves* an' things
   'At Ma don't 'low me to—
An' *chickun-gizzurds*—(don't like *wings*
   Like *Parunts* does! do *you?*)

2007

An' all the time, the wind blowed there,
An' I could feel it in my hair,
An' ist smell clover *ever*'where!—
   An' a' old red-head flew
Purt' nigh wite over my high-chair,
   When we et on the porch!

WILLY AND THE LADY

BY GELETT BURGESS

Leave the lady, Willy, let the racket rip,
She is going to fool you, you have lost your grip,
Your brain is in a muddle and your heart is in a whirl,
Come along with me, Willy, never mind the girl!

      Come and have a man-talk;
      Come with those who *can* talk;
Light your pipe and listen, and the boys will see you
    through;
      Love is only chatter,
      Friends are all that matter;
Come and talk the man-talk; that's the cure for you!

Leave the lady, Willy, let her letter wait,
You'll forget your troubles when you get it straight,
The world is full of women, and the women full of wile;
Come along with me, Willy, we can make you smile!

      Come and have a man-talk,
      A rousing black-and-tan talk,
There are plenty there to teach you; there's a lot for you
    to do;
      Your head must stop its whirling
      Before you go a-girling;
Come and talk the man-talk; that's the cure for you

WILLY AND THE LADY

Leave the lady, Willy, the night is good and long,
Time for beer and 'baccy, time to have a song;
Where the smoke is swirling, sorrow if you can—
Come along with me, Willy, come and be a man!

Come and have a man-talk,
Come with those who *can* talk,
Light your pipe and listen, and the boys will see you
through;
Love is only chatter,
Friends are all that matter;
Come and talk the man-talk; that's the cure for you!

Leave the lady, Willy, you are rather young;
When the tales are over, when the songs are sung,
When the men have made you, try the girl again;
Come along with me, Willy, you'll be better then!

Come and have a man-talk,
Forget your girl-divan talk;
You've got to get acquainted with another point of view!
Girls will only fool you;
We're the ones to school you;
Come and talk the man-talk; that's the cure for you!

A NEW YEAR IDYL

BY EUGENE FIELD

Upon this happy New Year night,
  A roach crawls up my pot of paste,
  And begs me for a tiny taste.
Aye, eat thy fill, for it is right
That while the rest of earth is glad,
  And bells are ringing wild and free,
  Thou shouldst not, gentle roachling, be
Forlorn and gaunt and weak and sad.

This paste to-night especially
  For thee and all thy kind I fixed,
  You'll find some whiskey in it mixed,
For which you have to thank but me.
So freely of the banquet take,
  And if you chance to find a drop
  Of liquor, prithee do not stop
But quaff it for thy stomach's sake.

Why dost thou stand upon thy head,
  All etiquette requirements scorning,
  And sing "You won't go home till morning"
And "Put me in my little bed"?
Your tongue, fair roach, is very thick,
  Your eyes are red, your cheeks are pale,
  Your underpinning seems to fail,
You are, I wot, full as a tick.

A NEW YEAR IDYL

ENVOI

I think I see that roach's home,
   That roach's wife, with broom in hand,
   That roach come staggering homeward and
Then all is glum and gloom and gloam.

A LAY OF ANCIENT ROME

BY THOMAS YBARRA

Oh! the Roman was a rogue,
  He erat, was, you bettum;
He ran his automobilis
  And smoked his cigarettum;
He wore a diamond studibus,
  An elegant cravattum,
A maxima cum laude shirt,
  And *such* a stylish hattum!

He loved the luscious hic-hæc-hock,
  And bet on games and equi;
At times he won; at others, though,
  He got it in the nequi;
He winked (quo usque tandem?)
  At puellas on the Forum,
And sometimes even made
  Those goo-goo oculorum!

He frequently was seen
  At combats gladiatorial,
And ate enough to feed
  Ten boarders at Memorial;
He often went on sprees
  And said, on starting homus,
"Hic labor—opus est,
Oh, where's my hic—hic—domus?"

A LAY OF ANCIENT ROME

Although he lived in Rome—
   Of all the arts the middle—
He was (excuse the phrase)
   A horrid individ'l;
Ah! what a diff'rent thing
   Was the homo (dative, hominy)
Of far-away B. C.
   From us of Anno Domini.

LITTLE BOPEEP AND LITTLE BOY BLUE

BY SAMUEL MINTURN PECK

It happened one morning that Little Bopeep,
While watching her frolicsome, mischievous sheep
Out in the meadow, fell fast asleep.

By her wind-blown tresses and rose-leaf pout,
And her dimpling smile, you'd have guessed, no doubt,
'Twas love, love, love she was dreaming about.

As she lay there asleep, came little Boy Blue,
Right over the stile where the daisies grew;
Entranced by the picture, he stopped in the dew.

So wildly bewitching that beautiful morn
Was Little Bopeep that he dropped his horn
And thought no more of the cows in the corn.

Our sorrows are many, our pleasures are few;
O moment propitious! What could a man do?
He kissed the wee lassie, that Little Boy Blue!

At the smack the woolies stood all in a row,
And whispered each other, "We're clearly *de trop;*
Such conduct is perfectly shocking—let's go!"

"FESTINA LENTE"

BY ROBERT J. BURDETTE

Blessings on thee, little man,
Hasten slowly as you can;
Loiter nimbly on your tramp
With the ten-cent speedy stamp.
Thou art "boss"; the business man
Postals writes for thee to scan;
And the man who writes, "With speed,"
Gets it—in his mind—indeed.

Lo, the man who penned the note
Wasted ten cents when he wrote;
And the maid for it will wait
At the window, by the gate,
In the doorway, down the street,
List'ning for thy footsteps fleet.
But her cheek will flush and pale,
Till it comes next day by mail,
With thine own indorsement neat—
"No such number on the street."
Oh, if words could but destroy,
Thou wouldst perish, truthful boy!

Oh, for boyhood's easy way—
Messenger who sleeps all day,
Or, from rise to set of sun,
Reads "The Terror" on the run.

ROBERT J. BURDETTE

For your sport, the band goes by;
For your perch, the lamp post high;
For your pleasure, on the street
Dogs are fighting, drums are beat;
For your sake, the boyish fray,
Organ grinder, run-away;
Trucks for your convenience are;
For your ease, the bob-tail car;
Every time and everywhere
You're not wanted, you are there.
Dawdling, whistling, loit'ring scamp,
Seest thou this ten-cent stamp?
Stay thou not for book or toy—
Vamos! Fly! Skedaddle, boy!

THE GENIAL IDIOT DISCUSSES LEAP YEAR

BY JOHN KENDRICK BANGS

"If I were a woman," said the Idiot, "I think that unless I had an affidavit from the man, sworn to before a notary and duly signed and sealed, stating that he did the proposing, I should decline to marry, or announce my engagement to be married in Leap Year. It is one of the drawbacks which the special privilege of Leap Year confers upon women that it puts them under suspicion of having done the courting if the thing comes out during the year."

"Don't you worry about that," laughed Mrs. Pedagog. "You can go through this country with a fine tooth comb and I'll wager you you won't find a woman anywhere who avails herself of the privilege who wouldn't have done the same thing in any old year if she wanted to. Of all the funny old superstitions, the quaintest of the lot is that Leap Year proposal business."

"How you talk," cried the Idiot. "Such iconoclasm. I had always supposed that Leap Year was a sort of matrimonial safety valve for old maids, and here in a trice you overthrow all the cherished notions of a lifetime. Why, Mrs. Pedagog, I know men who take to the woods every Leap Year just to escape the possibilities."

"Courageous souls," said the landlady. "Facing the unknown perils of the forest, rather than manfully meeting a proposal of marriage."

"It is hard to say no to a woman," said the Idiot. "I'd

hate like time to have one of 'em come to me and ask me to be hers. Just imagine it. Some dainty little damsel of a soulful nature, with deep blue eyes, and golden curls, and pearly teeth, and cherry lips, a cheek like the soft and ripening peach and a smile that would bewitch even a Saint Anthony, getting down on her knees and saying, 'O Idiot—dearest Idiot—be mine—I love you, devotedly, tenderly, all through the Roget's Thesaurusly, and have from the moment I first saw you. With you to share it my lot in life will be heaven itself. Without you a Saharan waste of Arctic frigidity. Wilt thou?' I think I'd wilt. I couldn't bring myself to say 'No, Ethelinda, I can not be yours because my heart is set on a strengthful damsel with raven locks and eyes of coal, with lips a shade less cherry than thine, and a cheek more like the apple than the peach, who can go out on the links and play golf with me. But if you ever need a brother in your business I am the floor-walker that will direct you to the bargain-counter where you'll find the latest thing in brothers at cost.' I'd simply cave in on the instant and say, 'All right, Ethelinda, call a cab and we'll trot around to the Little Church Around the Corner and tie the knot; that is, my love, if you think you can support me in the style to which I am accustomed."

Mr. Brief laughed. "I wouldn't bother if I were you, Mr. Idiot," said he. "Women don't tie up very strongly to Idiots."

"Oh don't they," retorted the Idiot. "Well, do you know I had a sort of notion that they did. The men that some of the nice girls I have known in my day have tied up to have somehow or other given me the impression that a woman has a special leaning toward Idiots. There was my old sweetheart, Sallie Wiggins, for instance—that wasn't her real name, of course, but she was one of the finest girls that ever attended a bargain sale. She had a mind far above the ordinary. She could read Schopenhauer at sight; understand Browning in a minute; her soul was as big as her heart and her heart was two and a half sizes larger than the universe. She was so strong-minded that although she could write poetry she wouldn't, and in the last year of her single blessedness she was the Queen-pin among the girls of her set. What she said was law, and emancipation of her sex was her only vice. Well, what do you think happened to Sallie Wiggins? After refusing every fine man in town, including myself,—I must say I only asked her five times; no telling what a sixth would have brought forth—she succumbed to the blandishments of the first sapheaded young Lochinvar that came out of the west, married him, and is now the smiling mother of nine children, does all the family sewing, makes her own parlor bric-a-brac out of the discarded utensils of the kitchen, dresses herself on ninety dollars a decade, and is happy."

"But if she loved him—" began the Lawyer.

"Impossible," said the Idiot. "She pitied him. She knew that if she didn't marry him, and take charge of him, another woman would, and that the chances were ten to one that the other woman wouldn't do the thing right and that Saphead's life would be ruined forever."

"But you say she is happy," persisted the Lawyer.

"Certainly she is," said the Idiot. "Because her life is an eternal sacrifice to Saphead's needs, and if there is a luxury in this mundane sphere that woman essentially craves it is the luxury of sacrifice. There is something fanatic about it. Sallie Wiggins voluntarily turned her back on seven men that I know of, one of whom is a Governor of his state; two of whom are now in Congress; one of whom is a judge of a state court; two of whom have become millionaire merchants; and the seventh of whom is to-day, probably, the most brilliant ornament of the penitentiary. Everyone of 'em turned down for Saphead, a man who parted his hair in the middle, couldn't earn seven dollars a century on his wits, is destined to remain hopelessly nothing, keeps her busy sewing buttons on his clothes, and to save his life couldn't tell the difference between Matthew Arnold and an automobile, and yet you tell me that women don't care for idiots."

"Miss Wiggins—or Mrs. Saphead, to be more precise," said Mr. Brief, "is only one instance."

"Well—there was Margaret Perkins—same town—same experience," said the Idiot. "Lovely girl—sought after by everybody—proposed to her myself five times—President of the Mental Culture Society of Baggville—graduate of Smythe—woman-member of Board of Education—Director of Young Girls' Institute—danced like a dream—had a sense of humor—laughed at my jokes—and married—what?"

"Well, what?" demanded the Lawyer.

"Prof. Omega Nit Zero, teacher of Cingalese in the University of Oklawaha, founded by a millionaire from Geneseo, New Jersey, who owned a hotel on the Oklawaha River that didn't pay, and hoped to brace up a bad investment by the establishment in the vicinity of a centre of culture. Prof. Zero receives ten dollars a week, and with his wife and three pupils constitutes the whole faculty, board of trustees, janitor, and student body of the University," said the Idiot. "Mrs. Zero dresses on nothing a year; cares for her five children on the same basis, and is happy. They are the principal patrons of the Oklawaha Hotel."

"Well—if she is happy?" said the Bibliomaniac.

"What business is it of anybody else? I think if Prof. Zero makes her happy he's the right kind of a man."

"You couldn't make Zero the right kind of a man," said the Idiot. "He isn't built that way. He wears men's clothes and he has sweet manners, and a dulcet voice, and the learning of the serpent; but when it comes to manhood he has the initiative of the turtle, lacking the cash value of the terrapin, or the turtle's mock brother; he wears a beard, but it is the beard of the bearded lady who up-to-date appears to be a useless appanage of the strenuous life; and when you try to get at his Americanism, if he has any, he flies off into stilted periods having to do with the superior virtues of the Cingalese. And Margaret Perkins that was hangs on his utterances as though he were a very archangel."

"Good," ejaculated Mr. Brief. "I am glad to hear that she is happy."

"So am I," said the Idiot. "But such happiness."

"Well, what's it all got to do with Leap Year, anyhow?" asked the Bibliomaniac.

"Nothing at all, except that it proves that girls aren't fitted really to choose their own husbands, and that therefore the special privilege conferred upon them by the recurrence of Leap Year should be rescinded by law," said the Idiot. "That privilege, owing to woman's incapacity to choose correctly, and man's weakness in the use of negatives, is a standing menace to the future happiness of the people."

"Hoity-toity," cried Mrs. Pedagog. "What a proposition. Tell me, Mr. Idiot, if a woman is not capable of selecting her own husband, who on earth is? Man himself—that embodiment of all the wisdom and all the sagacity of the ages?"

"I didn't say so," said the Idiot. "And I don't really

think so," he added. "The whole institution of getting engaged to be married should be regulated by the public authorities. Every county should have its Matrimonial Bureau, whose duty it should be to pair off all the eligible candidates in the matrimonial market, and in pairing them off it should be done on a basis of mutual fitness. Bachelors and old maids should be legislated out of existence, and nobody should be allowed to marry a second time until everybody else had been provided for. It is perfectly scandalous to me to read in the newspapers that a prominent widow in a certain town has married her third husband, when it is known that that same city contains 25,000 old maids who haven't the ghost of a show unless the State steps in and helps them out. What business has any woman to work up a corner in husbands, with so many of her sisters absolutely starving matrimonially?"

"And the young people are to have nothing to say about it, eh?" asked Mr. Brief.

"Oh yes—they can put in an application to the Bureau stating that they want to wed, and the Board of Managers can consider the desirability of issuing a permit," said the Idiot. "And they should be compelled to show cause why they should not be restrained from getting married. It is only in such a way that the state can reasonably guarantee the permanence of a contract to which it is in a sense a party. The State, by the establishment of certain laws, demands that the marriage contract shall practically be a life affair. It should therefore take it upon itself to see to it that there is a tolerable prospect at least that the contract is a just one. Many a poor woman has been bound to a life-long obligation of misery in which no consideration whatever has been paid by the party of the second part. If a contract without consideration will not stand in commerce, why should it in matrimony?"

"What you ought to go in for is Mormonism," snapped Mrs. Pedagog. "Keep on getting married until you've found just the right one and then get rid of all the others."

"That is a pleasing alternative," said the Idiot. "But expensive. I'd hate to pay a milliner's bill for a Mormon household—but anyhow we needn't grow acrimonious over the subject, for whatever I may think of matrimony as she exists to-day, all the injustices, inequalities, miseries of it, and all that, I prefer it to acrimony, and I haven't the slightest idea that my dream of perfect conditions will ever be realized. Only, Mary—"

"Yessir?" said the Maid.

"If between this and the first of January, 1905, any young ladies, or old ones either, call here and ask for me—"

"Yessir," said the Maid.

"Tell 'em I've gone to Nidjni-Novgorod and am not expected back for eleven years," said the Idiot. "I'm not going to take any chances."

COMPLETE INDEX

ALPHABETICALLY ARRANGED BY AUTHORS

COMPLETE INDEX